W9-CEE-301

PLOUGHSHARES

Winter 2014-15 • Vol. 40, No. 4

Ploughshares, a journal of new writing, is guest-edited serially by prominent writers who explore different personal visions, aesthetics, and literary circles. *Ploughshares* is published in April, August, and December at Emerson College: 120 Boylston Street, Boston, MA 02116-4624. Telephone: (617) 824-3757. Web address: pshares.org. E-mail: pshares@pshares.org.

Subscriptions (ISSN 0048-4474): $35 for one year (3 issues and 1 Solos *Omnibus*), $55 for two years (6 issues and 2 Solos *Omnibuses*), and $70 for three years (9 issues and 3 Solos *Omnibuses*); $50 a year for institutions. Add $35 a year for international postage ($15 for Canada and Mexico).

Upcoming: Spring 2015, an international poetry issue edited by Neil Astley, will be published in April 2015. Fall 2015, a fiction issue edited by Lauren Groff, will be published in July. Solos *Omnibus Volume 3* will be published in October 2015. Winter 2015-16, a staff-edited poetry and prose issue, will be published in January 2016.

Submissions: The regular reading period is from June 1 to January 15 (postmark and online dates). All submissions sent from January 16 to May 31 will be returned unread. From March 1 to May 15, we also read for our Emerging Writer's Contest. Please see page 218 for editorial and submission policies, or visit our website: pshares.org/submit.

Back-issue, classroom-adoption, and bulk orders may be placed directly through Ploughshares. *Ploughshares* is also available as full-text products from EBSCO, H.W. Wilson, JSTOR, ProQuest, and the Gale Group. Indexed in M.L.A. Bibliography, Humanities International Index, and Book Review Index. Full publishers' index is online at pshares.org. The views and opinions expressed in this journal are solely those of the authors. All rights for individual works revert to the authors upon publication. Ploughshares receives support from the National Endowment for the Arts and the Massachusetts Cultural Council.

Retail distribution by Ingram Periodicals, Media Solutions, Ubiquity, and Disticor Direct in Canada. Printed in the U.S.A. by The Sheridan Press.

CONTENTS

Winter 2014-15

EMERGING WRITER'S CONTEST WINNERS

Cover: Philip Geiger, *Different Shirt*, 2006, oil on board, 24" x 18". Courtesy of Tibor de Nagy Gallery, New York, NY.

Elegy for No One

So many have died,
to pick just one
seems willful,
unkind, and besides
you might forget
the friend you promised
never to forget,
so let this be
for anyone who died
in this season of death,
which from now on
will be full of faces
coming forward,
smiling from the page
like the line hastily
formed backstage
that stands before
the curtain, and bows,
then follows its spot
into the shade
of scenery and props.

KEITH ALTHAUS

On a Photograph of Gurdjieff in a Bookstore Window

The dome, the mustache
like a circus strongman's,
those shoulders people still climb on,
and eyes that hold you
in the snow before stacked
and battered volumes of mutually
exclusive systems of belief:
UFOs, black magic, Madame
Blavatsky's wisdom received
at the feet of lamas, while
yours grow cold in the slushy street.
His look follows passersby
who, though they can't identify
the man or recognize
the eyes which leapt
to music, movement, dance,
still stop on the sidewalk
as if on command.

JEANNE MARIE BEAUMONT
Fifteen Views of a Christening Gown

That it was fine linen flawlessly stitched,
    as silken as new skin.

That it was the color of ivory or an old book's pages
    left blank in the front.

In the beginning shape of the letter A, it made
    a long A sound. With lace.

Because she was heard to say it had been passed
    down. *Saved.* This was not the first.

That it draped abundantly, way way past
    the babe's curled-in feet.

That it contained. And it concealed.

As a sacramental dress, it too had been blessed.

That it came with a matching hat, beribboned.

That it was closed with the agitations of pearls,
    buttons aglow like infant nails.

That it was a small bride. Something borrowed
    that embraced something blue.

That it smelled as clean as God.

April it was. A long long aching shape.

Because she could not forget, they remembered.

That it was the last. Not first.

Because she was heard to say, *we buried her in it.*

JEANNE MARIE BEAUMONT
Portrait with Closed Eyes

She was the stain in the teacup
    that spread up toward the handle.
She was the handle that snapped
    off the hairbrush, and
She was the hairbrush he tossed
    onto the fire, and
She was the fire he carried
    each day in his pipe.

She was the pipe the bath water
    rode to the river, and
She was the river where they
    boarded the boat to limbo.
She was the limbo that held
    the secreted acorns, and
She was the acorn that
    bruised his weary knees.

She was the knees that knocked
    beneath the oak table, and
She was the table where glasses
    were refilled till midnight.
She was the midnight that darkened
    the brow of the child,
Child who never felt safe indoors,
    who never felt safe outdoors.

She, the heaviest of doors, was the reason.
    She was their stain.

REMICA BINGHAM-RISHER
If It's Magic

When I find the *Songs in the Key of Life* 45s
I marvel at the messages my parents inscribed:

Sweet Dee and Junior Bee—In Love '79
their marks on the sheath's concentric circles,

inside, on the lyrics booklet, worn smooth
their scratches on the grooves.

I spend a year playing the set
enthralled every few days by some new epithet—

a background voice trailing,
a tone's shift or timbre—

my mother counts the years since their beginning,
how I interrupt their ending, our common

heartache and revelry,
what each of us remembers.

The strange obsessions I inherit:
their soulful cinders, indecipherable

refrains, this awful insistence
on fraught and ordinary pain.

Next Year in Juarez

The last time this type of celestial event was visible from Earth was more than seven hundred years ago. The Dark Ages. Dante was at work on the *Commedia*, writing in the mornings, breaking at noon to masturbate and have his tea, then back at his desk until dusk. King Philip IV ordered the kidnapping of Pope Boniface, had him beaten, taunted, and threatened with castration before letting him walk, after which he shortly died. Next, King Philip IV expelled the Jews from France. These events having no causal relation of which we are aware. One night over the spires of Avignon, over the mountains of Ethiopia, above the narrow sandy mouth where the Yellow River empties into the Bohai Sea, six thousand meteors burned sideways and fast across a sky already luminous with stars. The Aztecs land in Tenochtitlán. The Hundred Years' War begins.

Javier left the stack of ungraded midterms on his desk and said a stern goodbye to Saint-Simon, his doubletail betta fish who a week ago had murdered her bowl mate. He poked his head in the other TA's office to return a borrowed Bourdieu, then cut out early to beat the dreaded Houston rush hour. Javier was in his third year of graduate study to become a historian, which in 2013 was as sensible as saying you would like to become an apothecary.

But tonight was the night he was going to propose to Nalani. He couldn't afford a ring yet, so instead he would give her a meteor shower. She had no idea what was coming; he'd only said they were going out for the night to celebrate her return home from Haiti. In their three years together she had let him surprise her many times and often, he could admit, in grandiose ways. But this was different. This was the universe going over the top—his role in it was simple. At home he stashed what they would need in a backpack and took it down to the car: plastic glasses, a bottle of wine, a big wool blanket, and the binoculars that his father had given him years ago. Heavy vintage Bushnells his father used to wear around his neck to baseball games and pass to Javier so he could see the tiny left fielder crouch in fine, stereoscopic detail, see the pleats in his pants, the wrinkles in his jersey. His father, who had never proposed to his mother. The baseball fanatic and fearless journalist who had been dead almost ten years, struck down in the street by a police bullet while covering the labor union protests in Mexico City. His death had been almost surely unintentional, though this made no difference to the popular Left, who still celebrated him as a great martyr. "Every shot fired from a gun has someone's name on it," said Diderot in 1756.

"Are we going somewhere outside? Maybe I'll get some hash," Nalani said. She was standing in the lamplight of their bedroom, removing her bra. She had lost a little weight again in Haiti, her third and most frustrating trip this year. The NGO's funding had dried up, and she was the lead grant writer. It was a regular and permanent fact of their lives now, her flights to Port-au-Prince, but Javier still remembered the first time she left, how scared he was for her, how afraid he was for himself, of what he'd lose if anything happened to her on that wild and broken island, still smoking from where the earth had ruptured and cracked open and threatened to drown everyone in fire and sea. Javier twisted the wheels on the ocular lenses until Nalani's nipples were perfectly in focus. Black as a night with no moon.

"¿Las drogas por nosotros?" Javier said. Neither of them had smoked in a long time. He didn't want her stoned when he got down on one knee and delivered the elegant sentence he still hadn't quite perfected.

"Lisa more or less requires it," Nalani said, wiggling into her jeans.

"Wait, you invited Lisa?" he said.

"Yeah, why wouldn't I?"

"I thought we could have a night alone," he said.

Nalani looked at him suspiciously. "What's up your sleeve?"

"Nothing. Let her come. I'm glad she's coming." He watched his girlfriend watching herself in the mirror as she clothed her long, beautiful body. "You're gonna want a sweatshirt," he said.

Nalani moved closer until her stomach almost touched the binoculars. He refocused so he could see the minuscule grooves in her skin. An Englishman named Robert Hooke discovered the cell in 1655, staring through a crude lens at bits of cork. He called them cells because they made him think of the cramped domiciles of monks. Nalani lowered the binoculars with her hand, gently. She shrieked, then laughed as Javier scooped her around the waist and heaved her over his shoulder onto the bed.

Lisa was Nalani's old friend from Cornell. She had finished her doctorate in Vienna and had recently accepted a prestigious laboratory job in Houston and Nalani had been inviting her everywhere they went. It was sort of like they'd adopted a thirty-year-old foreign exchange student who had more money than they did. Which was all right with Javier, because he liked Lisa. She was smart and had lived all over Europe and spoke all the languages and was socially conscious on issues Javier hadn't even known were issues to be conscious about, such as bottled water, and mental health parity, and not putting cat litter in plastic bags. Javier liked to tell her that she was making good penance for having been born a white devil. "It's not your fault," he would tell her. "We forgive you," Nalani would say.

Before they left, Nalani took a call and went out onto the balcony and Javier watched her through the glass. She'd started cheating on cigarettes again in Haiti and she lit one, leaning over the railing. Javier imagined her thirty years from now, still thin but in a long wraparound instead of jeans, her braids going gray, and the image he called up made him feel a somber kind of peace. Where he was rashly insecure and chased by self-doubt, she was salty, methodical, and had an almost lordly equanimity. He thought of the first time he saw her, at a gallery show where an awful experimental noise band was playing and where Javier, tipsy, had offered her a cigarette out on the sidewalk and insulted the music only to hear her respond that the guy playing the circuit-bent cello was her date. He watched her laughing through the balcony glass and imagined her pregnant, hand on the curve of her belly, smiling at him just as she was right now, only without the smoke wriggling up from her fingers. There were still a lot of ways he couldn't conjure her. He would love her his whole life and never get to the bottom.

She slid open the door and came inside. "Hash is a go."

Javier took them all for paella at a new Spanish place off West Gray, where they sat at the bar and Nalani pressed Lisa for updates on the Samantha Situation. Lisa had only been out for a couple years and was always in some calamitous relationship, and Javier liked hearing about her drama. He and Nalani were so steady, such natural partners that hearing about someone else's romantic turbulence was somehow invigorating, like hearing a stranger talk about the dangerous city you used to live in but haven't visited for years. After dinner they walked to the art house cinema, where Javier had meant for them to see the new Woody Allen film—a madcap romance set in Rome. But when they got there, Lisa insisted that they see *Battle of Algiers*. Nalani cried twice during the film. Javier thought the movie was excellent, but it was long and exhausting and nowhere near the mood he had intended to set. Still, it was a distraction from his nerves, which otherwise would've been unbearable. He let himself be transported by the film, forgetting the big moment to come, forgetting Nalani, keeping all those feelings in reserve for later. It almost felt like a typical night.

"So much glamour in those kinds of wars," Javier said, as the three of them walked out of the quiet theater, "I find myself trying so hard not to romanticize it."

"He says, while totally romanticizing it," Nalani said.

"Girl, please," said Javier.

Lisa was gazing out at the glimmering lights of downtown. "You guys want to go to The Mink?" she smiled hopefully.

"We can't tonight," Javier said quickly.

"Why not?" Nalani said.

"Just follow me," he said, and turned to walk.

Nalani jostled Lisa's arm teasingly as they crossed the street. "Let her wonder where you are," Nalani said.

Samantha was Lisa's most recent ex-girlfriend, a Belgian folksinger who had followed her here to Houston uninvited. When Lisa reacted with understandable alarm, Samantha rented an apartment anyway and began playing sets in all the bars in their neighborhood, dating women three at a time in a sexual offensive, as if she was trying to claim every young lesbian in Houston before Lisa could get her bags unpacked. The Belgian Invasion, Javier had called it.

Nalani announced for the second time that she had not enjoyed the paella. There were bones in her fish. Walking behind the girls, Javier mulled over the book he hoped his dissertation would become. A daring reevaluation of twentieth-century insurgencies worldwide, from the Salvadoran Peasant Massacre to the campaigns of Che to Hamas. It was the type of work his department liked to sneer at, more social criticism or political theory than hard-core historical research. But if he could define the abstractions with grace and force, make them crystallize, it would be a very important book. His notion of "radical empathy" could recast the debate for the West, force a new term into the stale dialectic of terrorists, states, and ideologies. He, it, could transfigure the dominant political realism of his era. This, Javier knew, was the real reason his professors were so critical of it. It was sloppy, they told him, and would never get published. They wanted him to be as small and ordinary and fastidious as they were themselves. But Javier did not want to be a sterile academic. He wanted to be a dangerous thinker, a public intellectual, no more a historian from Texas than Marx was an economist from Trier. And who better than Nalani, the firebrand activist, the person who had inspired the very idea of radical empathy, to be his partner and wife? They would be theory and praxis in the flesh.

It was dark for their long walk from one end of West Gray to the other. Javier slipped his arm around Nalani's waist and when they got to the café on the corner, he guided her inside.

"Disgusting," Lisa said as they stood in line for coffee. "That war. The slaughter of children."

"Too long by half an hour," Nalani said.

"Everyone should have listened to Camus," Javier said.

"Galveston?" Nalani said, when Javier steered them onto southbound I-45. Javier could hear the hollow effort in her voice. Though she'd been back three days, she was still tired from her trip—not even the espresso had helped. There was a traffic jam on the causeway and Javier had to rev the little car in rocking starts up the steep bridge. It was easy to imagine them giving in to gravity, rolling backward, smashing into the cars behind. At the top of the causeway, they could see that the whole descent onto the island was a string of red taillights. A clear spring night over the waxy, dimpled bay.

"Are all these people doing the same thing we're doing?" Nalani said.

"I didn't know Texans were so adventurous," said Lisa, from the backseat.

"We're an outdoorsy people but this ends up creating lots of traffic," Javier said. He was trying to text Lisa as he drove, without letting Nalani see. *When I give you the signak,* he typed, *Give uf some spave.* He waited for the beep of Lisa's phone, watching her in the rearview, but she stared out the window lost in some worry or fantasy. When the beep finally came, she did not seem to notice.

They made it to the seawall and walked down to the dark beach where tribes of people were gathered around small fires and gas lanterns, shouting and laughing over the sounds of radios and drunken horse-play, the bark of dogs. A group of colorful people were gathered around lawn chairs and already holding signs up to the sky, though it was barely past ten o'clock. The signs were done in glow-in-the-dark letters and said things like "COME TO ME MY DARLINGS" and "WE ARE NOT LIKE THE OTHERS." A fat man in a Texans jersey was grilling hotdogs. Two little sugar-high blond children ran shrieking between Nalani and Lisa, the girl terrorizing her brother, her fingers locked over her ears like horns. They walked past a sober trio of women who seemed to be quarreling politely as they set up telescopes and lab-grade camera equipment. From the opposite direction, a man walked by them in the edge of the surf, calling out for "Quincy" in a grim voice. Javier led the three of them past the campfires, far out beyond the hotels to a deserted bank of sand and spread out their blanket. It was a little windy, but the Gulf night was dense and warm and the wine made it warmer. They laid on their backs a few feet from shore and looked up at the sky, black and thick as custard. There was no moon. This, Javier thought, was perfect. Nalani lit a joint and passed it to Javier, who immediately passed it across to Lisa.

"Those binoculars are not going to show you much," Lisa said.

Javier thought about it for a minute, held the lenses to his eyes, saw abject darkness. He felt like an idiot. He put the binoculars behind them, out of sight. "I know," he said. "I just brought them to weigh down our blanket."

Nalani laughed through her nose. "Is there supposed to be an eclipse or something?" she said.

"How have you not heard about this?" Lisa said, blowing on the cherry so it roasted brightly in the dark.

"I been in Haiti, man," Nalani said.

"Don't tell her," Javier said to Lisa.

"Yeah, don't tell me," Nalani said.

They laid there like three mystics waiting for the sky to erupt, and they talked about Samantha and the virtues of reckless love. Javier tried to listen but he had become nervous, all at once, that Nalani would say no. He needed her more than ever. Something about Lisa being here made him see that. He took a light drag from the joint to calm the skipping muscle in his chest.

Javier thought he saw a meteor but it was only the blinking light of a plane making incremental progress through the night. He listened to the still-cold waves folding over in their meek little rows. There was nothing to fear.

"What if you had to choose between love and the revolution?" Nalani said to him, knocking his feet with hers. "Comes down to one moment. There you are in the spotlight. It's me or the struggle."

"The *Casablanca* problem," Javier said. The hash was making the words slow down in his mouth so he could feel each syllable form like its own object, a strange, sculpted, original thing. "*Rick…*" he said, in his Peter Lorre whine. "*Hide* me, please."

"Stop stalling," Lisa said. From the other side of the blanket her voice was thin and far away.

"I'd pick you, every time," Javier said, finding Nalani's warm fingers in the dark. He sounded sentimental, he knew, but tonight was a night to be sentimental.

"He's the Anti-Bogart," Lisa said.

"I don't know," Nalani said. Her slender body was between him and Lisa, but she seemed to occupy more significant space than they did, like she was the main idea of the blanket. "Sometimes people hide out in love," she said. "Hide from the world. It can be a kind of selfishness. Like if Rick had gone with Ilsa. You fall in love and all you see, all you want to see is yourself reflected back in the other person. Meanwhile, the world is on fire."

"Nietzsche says it's only in love that we can forget ourselves entirely, therefore only love has within it the truth of the knowledge of death," Javier said.

"Yeah," Lisa said. "Because when I want to understand erotic love, I open my Nietzsche."

"Don't be scared of him," said Javier. "He had syphilis. He knew."

He heard Lisa flicking the lighter, trying to get another joint going, but the wind wasn't letting it spark.

There were hundreds of stars but none of them would move. Javier decided he would do it soon no matter what. Maybe the astronomers had gotten it wrong. But he always felt lucky and brave when he came to Galveston. For five wild years after 1817, until Andrew Jackson finally had enough, this island was the pirate colony of the sensational Lafitte brothers, their haven in Spanish Texas for revolutionaries, smugglers, and slavers. The brothers' politics was not discerning—ill-gotten gold was their lone criterion of alliance. Every inch of the beach the three of them were lying on had been dug up time and again by parties in search of that treasure.

"Let's play the game," Lisa said.

"What game?" Javier said. She had to have seen his text by now.

"You have to name things that aren't worth being afraid of," Nalani explained. "We used to play this all night in the dorm at Cornell, and it took forever because Lisa isn't scared of anything."

"But if someone names something you are afraid of, you have to admit it, and drink everyone's liquor," Lisa said.

"And then we laugh at you," Nalani said.

"You start," Lisa said to Javier.

"Alien abductions," he offered.

"Poisonous snakes," said Nalani.

"Resounding failure in one's chosen professional field," Javier said.

"Horrible disfigurement of the body," Nalani said.

"I'm afraid of that," said Javier, raising his glass. Nalani had shown him pictures of earthquake victims in Haiti, little kids with severed limbs and shrunken heads, women with burns covering their bodies like a second skin. The kinds of injuries he would rather die from than be asked to sustain.

Lisa finally got the joint lit. Then she let out a little cry of surprise, pointing high up over their heads. It was beginning.

Javier was gazing at another solitary faint blinking tracer when he heard a man's voice carrying on the moist and salty wind. The voice got closer and closer, and then it was right behind them, a young man's voice.

"That's what I thought. Y'all found my binoculars."

Javier craned his neck around. There were six of them and they all had their shirts off, their white chests and shoulders a hazy pale blue in the darkness. Javier wasn't sure, but it looked like a few of them were wearing makeup or war paint or maybe some kind of camouflage. Another one said, "This is a private beach."

Javier started to get to his feet, but they crowded in on every side and the guy who spoke first came rushing in fast like he was going to drop-kick Lisa in the head. He stopped right before and laughed in a high, strained cackle. The kid was shorter than the others but muscular and stocky, and his bald head veered around rhythmically, like he was hearing some hypnotic music in his head. Nalani sat up so Javier did too. He couldn't see much in the dark but he could smell them, their onrushing stink of booze and sweat and something else, a fever. Nalani let go of his hand.

"What'd you take my binoculars for?" the bald one said.

"These are mine," said Javier, realizing he was clutching them tightly with both hands. Then he added, "Did you really lose a pair?" and made a show of looking up the dark beach as if they might be lying around somewhere, stranded among the seaweed.

The bald one kicked sand in Javier's face.

"Just leave us alone," Nalani said. Several of them laughed in that same high cackle. They were out of high school but not by much, teenagers with no belief in consequences.

"Look. We're here to watch the astronomical event," said Javier. He realized that talking like one of their teachers was his only plan to make himself seem like a real person.

"This guy's a fucking faggot," said someone behind him.

The bald one was pacing now, swearing at Javier, getting more and more enraged as he slapped his own chest. He kept saying the same unintelligible phrase over and over, gnashing the words, his voice rising an octave.

All the kids were shouting now as if this was what they had come to see. Like Javier was the Christian in a gladiator ring. "Do it, Mason!"

Javier stayed propped on his elbows. He knew the second he got to his feet they'd be all over him. One of the kids gave a twisting kick and a wall of sand flew up, swept over them all. Nalani shouted in protest.

Mason was standing still now, his arms held out open at his sides like a priest. Then he pointed at Javier's face.

"You guys are pathetic. This is stupid," said Lisa.

For a second there was a brittle silence. Javier could not believe she said that. As if she was the one who'd have to back it up. He felt the need to apologize for her. Then everyone was in motion. Somebody ripped the binoculars out of Javier's hand as another yanked him by the hood of his sweatshirt, dragging him backward off the blanket.

"OK, OK" Javier said, getting to his feet, stepping carefully over Nalani and in front of the one called Mason. "Look," Javier said. He trembled. "We don't want any trouble at all. Please. Just leave."

Mason took a small step away and then lurched into Javier's gut. Javier caught one of his own teeth wrong and almost bit it out. He was on his knees with all his wind knocked out, as if his whole torso was sealed shut. He let out a croak for air but none came for an excruciating minute, and during that minute, he knew he would suffocate, his fists squeezing mounds of damp sand. It was taking too long for him to breathe. He heard Nalani yelling something. Or Lisa. Both their voices mingling in the same frequency of panic.

When Javier could finally breathe, it was too late. The kids were ripping through his pockets for his wallet and phone. A thin kid with a mouth of smeared paint grabbed the car keys off the blanket and got up close to Javier's face and shook the keys, smiled, then whipped Javier across the eyes. Javier held his face in his hands and someone pushed his head down into the sand, and as Nalani and Lisa were cursing, someone kicked him in the ear. He lay there, a roundness of shock forcing his eyes wide open into the sand. The keys dropped on the back of his head and slid coldly down his neck.

"Monkey nigger!" one of them yelled at Nalani, and then they all started yelling it like a chant, surrounding her and Lisa. Nalani was screaming now in a voice that was feral and raw and that Javier had never heard before. He saw them grabbing her by the shoulders and twisting her by the feet while Mason leaned over and slowly felt at her pockets, his hands heavy and mocking. When he reached for her breasts, Nalani ripped an arm free and knocked his hands away. "Get the fuck away from her!" Javier screamed, his voice stripped and weak. Lisa yelled that she was calling the cops, but then her cries were muffled. Someone's fingers were still tightening around Javier's neck. Nalani was snarling. The kids let out a whoop, laughing as she fought one-handed. A loud pop— Nalani had smacked Mason on his face with her open palm. Mason stumbled back and stood upright, stunned. The hand released his neck and Javier felt around in the darkness for the metal corkscrew. He was going to kill them all. Mason loomed over Nalani, wordless, and for an instant everything hovered and seemed to expand. Javier gazed into the pale of Mason's throat. His fingers closed around cold metal.

And then they were gone, roaming in a pack down the beach. They went as quick as they came, walking farther west away from the hotels, deeper into the darkness, and soon they were out of sight. Javier watched himself running after them, skimming barefoot down the beach and hitting Mason in the back of the head with the wine bottle. Cracking his skull apart, hammering it into dust. But he hadn't moved. His body was shaking in spasms, and he went down on one knee to where Nalani sat pulling slow, even breaths.

Lisa was standing a few feet away, close to the water, holding herself by her elbows. "Where are the keys? Do we have keys?" Lisa said. She was wandering back and forth, but she wasn't looking at anything.

Javier couldn't see Nalani's face. "Are you OK?" he said, touching her arm. His hand was shaking and he could barely speak.

"I'm fine," she said, and the flatness of her voice was a shock in the dark, and just then high up behind her a great white light sped throbbing through the sky.

Javier gunned it over the bridge too fast. "Motherfucking animals." His hands were shaking so violently, waving really, he had to bring his knee up to the steering wheel to keep control. He angled his face away from the girls and tried to breathe.

Lisa leaned up from the backseat and peered at the dashboard. "Can you slow down?" she said.

"We should've called the fucking cops," Javier said, weaving around a sluggish van.

"No, we shouldn't have" Nalani said. "There's a hundred kids on that beach. You want them to round up the usual suspects?"

"Yeah," Lisa said, as if they were discussing something normal. "I think it would've done more harm than good."

Javier slammed the steering wheel with his fist. Lisa's head retreated. Nalani reached over and put her hand on the back of Javier's neck and pressed her fingers there for a long time, kneading surely into the skin.

For days afterward Javier was despondent and sore, staring into books without reading, staring out the living-room window at the chinaberry trees while a dim white noise rose and fell in his mind. On Monday morning he tried to go to campus but the drive was a nightmare—every turn a head-on collision. He startled at phantom horns bleating in outrage each time he changed lanes on the highway. By the time he pulled into the parking lot, he was late for his class and too racked with dread to get out of the car. His students would be eyeing the whiteboard, texting their friends, wondering when they could get up and leave. Their midterms still untouched on his office desk. He sat there for a while as if listening for a voice to speak, then drove slowly out the backside of campus along the bayou. A mile from home, he jerked against his seatbelt at the blast of a slow-moving train, the clang of harsh bells, and he was staring at the blinking red lights of the lowered crossing arms, the same red as the taillights strung out in front of him, when he realized he was crying.

He didn't leave the house again for days. He woke one morning midweek in an empty bed. Nalani was in the kitchen with her oatmeal, sliding her finger rapidly over her tablet on the table. Javier stood at the coffee pot but it was switched off and cold. "Don't you think there was something about those kids that was evil? Unreal, almost. They literally emerged out of the darkness," he said.

"We couldn't have done anything different," she said.

"What if we had? What if I'd had a weapon? We didn't know if they did or not."

Nalani blew on her spoon. "Baby, can we please talk about something else?"

He went back to their bedroom and closed the door. When she came in to dress for work, he rolled over and pretended to be asleep.

Later, alone, Javier began to call up friends and tell the story over and over, pacing, with the phone on his ear, from the kitchen to the bedroom, up and down the hall. "It was so bizarre," he always began. He would loathe himself with each repetition, but he couldn't stop. The more times Javier answered the same questions, the more perplexed and furious he became by the simplicity of what had happened, its lack of any hidden logic.

A few times, he caught himself in the middle of a strange action. One night while waiting for the teakettle to boil he touched his fingers to the red-hot coils, on purpose but without really thinking. He shouted in pain and Nalani came rushing in. "Accident," he said. She took his hand and held it under the faucet without a word, and he felt like a child as he stood there beside her, listening to the run of the tap. Another time, as a friend offered by-now familiar theories about the assault, Javier took a steak knife from the sink and sliced across the palm of his hand. The blood took a dreadfully long second to rise.

By the end of the week, he and Nalani weren't eating dinner together or going to bed at the same time. She'd go in their room at night and

Javier, from his chair down the hall, would see the thin glowing line around the door and it would feel like a tense standoff between them until the light went out. He knew she was enduring daily crises at work, just from the length of her evening showers he knew, but her refusal to talk about the incident at the beach felt like a punctuation mark on some awful judgment, the terms of which Javier could not clearly see. He felt as if he was living in their apartment alone.

One night, he was in the bathtub when Nalani came home. It was late. He'd cancelled his classes for the fourth day in a row and had spent it smoking hash cigarettes and pulling books off the shelves, five or six of which were piled around the bathroom floor. He was on the phone again. "You could feel the evil coming off of them like fumes," Javier said. "My book, my whole theory is falling apart. I'm looking at it like, what the hell have I been writing? Is this a joke? All of it, all of it is worthless."

He heard Nalani come to the bathroom door and pause, then walk to their bedroom and slam the door shut.

"I don't feel sure of anything anymore," Javier said. "Only that I had this corkscrew in my hand and I knew I was going to stab these kids. It was in my entire body, this imperative to kill. It was like I had become as savage as them," Javier said. "They would've deserved it too," he said. "Maybe not in a courtroom, but if you had been there…" The friend tried to say something but Javier cut him off. "You see why people here walk around with guns. Nobody has the right to just come and do that to you. To terrorize you for their own deranged pleasure." The friend said he was just glad no one was hurt. "If they hadn't run off," Javier said, "That beach would've had dead fucking kids."

Then Nalani was in the bathroom, looking at him. Javier told his friend he'd call him back and he let the phone drop on the floor.

"You have to stop," Nalani said. "This is driving me crazy."

"What is that supposed to mean?"

"You're obsessed. And I need you to stop," she said. "Did you teach your classes today? What really happened to your hand?"

"I'm not obsessed. I'm just trying to fully understand…"

"You don't need to understand shit, you need to talk it up till you don't feel like a coward anymore."

The water in the tub had gone cold and Javier pulled his knees to his chest. "But they were the real thing, they were actual evil, evil without any purpose or responsibility, evil in a tourniquet—" He felt as if he was losing control, the words spilling out from some murky access of his mind.

"It was just a robbery," Nalani said. Her voice was pitiless and calm. "They were kids. Stupid drunk kids."

He was reaching for the volume of Hannah Arendt on the floor but his arm knocked the ashtray off its ledge. The stubs of hashish cigarettes floated in the bath. "—Because they're the ones who refuse self-knowledge and that's where real villainy comes from, where genocide and—"

"LISTEN to yourself!" Nalani said.

Javier stared at her. Her hazel eyes were still and not cruel, and Javier knew from the swoop in his gut that she was about to bring it up.

"I've *had* shit done to me," she said. "And what happened to us last week was scary for about a minute and then it was nothing. Nothing. You're fine, I'm fine, Lisa's fine."

Whenever Nalani made reference to that particular episode of her past, something in him felt ashamed, though he wasn't sure exactly why. Maybe ashamed on behalf of all men, or because he had nothing to say to make it any less sick that it had happened, or because he knew that he did not and would never understand what it must have felt like for a nine-year-old girl to suffer that. Or because he'd catch himself scrutinizing these failures of his as she was still talking, trying to tell him how she felt in her measured voice, but he couldn't hear her for all the vain, analytical natter in his head. Her bringing it up in this context, though, made him angry. It wasn't fair to bring it up now.

He stood up out of the tub in front of her. Water dripped from his body all over the open white face of *The Wretched of the Earth*. He stood there, naked, staring at the fine braids of Nalani's hair, the line of glistening sweat on her brow. "My dad's binoculars are gone," he said. "Forever."

"I don't think I'm in love with you anymore," she said.

His eyes fell to her waist, then to the floor. He realized he was staring at a line of moving water as it spread in a thin column and made for Nalani's bare brown toes, as if its will was to reach her. Somehow he already knew everything.

"I didn't cheat on you, but I want to start seeing another person," she said.

"Haiti?"

She nodded slightly. "He lives here, though."

It was very quiet in the bathroom. He could hear the steam moving in the air between them.

"I was going to ask you to marry me that night."

"I know," she said. "That's why I had Lisa come."

He took the towel she gave him and dropped it at her feet.

Most meteors are smaller than a grain of sand. They originate as the dust trails of comets orbiting the sun, then begin to orbit the comet, then finally move into our path. Or we move into theirs. Or it's a bit of both. What we are seeing is the vaporization of cosmic dust as it makes contact with our atmosphere—the cloud that keeps us alive by letting us breathe. What this contact looks like, from our perspective, is a departure.

CHRISTOPHER BUCKLEY
Lost Music

Contrails crisscrossing overhead,
spreading puff by fading puff
into each instant of the past...
dull notes, antiphonal clouds lined out
against the blue, arpeggios
down that road as far
as we can hope to go...
                              The dish
ran away with the spoon, your mother
at the linoleum table, humming
that rhyme in the kitchen—
fried baloney, a tin of tomato soup,
that apartment on Micheltorena
a block from the park. You were staring
into the purple GE plastic radio
the size of a breadbox, its golden dial
pulling in the themes to *Gunsmoke,*
The Lone Ranger, or your father's voice
on KDB with a lead-in to June Christy
and "That's All"...The world fixed
and regular as the bells recorded
for the Five Star Final at 5:00,
as the dark descending down the foothills
with your bedtime, from where
you had no idea...
                              The great minds
of antiquity believed in an entrance
to the underworld past The Pillars of Hercules,
at least, you figured, somewhere south
of Los Angeles as you studied your Bible History
text.
          Then, the next thing you knew,
your mother gone and no way back

to the black & white '50s, the orchestral
underscoring of those gray medieval clouds
carried along with Gregorian chants,
incense hovering, your weedy voice then
and forever, dissolving in the smoky
benediction of the air. When were you
supposed to find time to understand
the music of the spheres? Where
were you going to go from there?

DAVID CAMERON
Mannequin

Oscar bought a mannequin so he could drive the HOV lane at rush hour. He bid her off eBay and dressed her in an oversize pantsuit that his wife hadn't worn since college. She had jagged cheekbones and a black wig. She was lean. His wife, Daphne, called her Dora.

"Dora?" Oscar asked, staring at his wife, hands at his sides, awaiting her logic.

"The Explorer. The kids' show."

"You think this is odd," Oscar said, "but it isn't. It's a practical solution to a real problem."

She nodded, because it was. Last spring, Oscar lost his manufacturing-engineering position in Manchester, New Hampshire, after only two years. It was the longest position he'd held in a decade. He spent the summer on unemployment before finally securing a similar gig for a firm in Braintree, Massachusetts—an arrangement that required driving straight through Boston at the worst possible times both morning and evening. No matter how he arranged his schedule, traffic was a three-lane clogged artery both coming and going, while the High Occupancy Vehicle lane, reserved for cars with at least two occupants, hummed along smugly. A commuting partner would solve the problem.

Daphne found a car-pooling website that matched up local commuters. But the thought of squeezing into a Toyota for three hours a day with strangers caused a tingling unease. People, with their smells and banter and breakfast crumbs—he'd rather stay unemployed.

And so he purchased a fiberglass mannequin from a New Jersey warehouse for $160. Wig included.

After the UPS truck delivered the box, he closed the garage door and took inventory of the parts. "Dora" came in five separate pieces. He sat her right-leg/buttocks combo on a small stepladder, screwed in the left leg, then attached the torso—disappointed to find the head didn't move. Last were the arms. There she sat in the garage, naked and tanned, legs tightly crossed, hands over the knees, her torso curved in a posture that clearly required the engagement of belly muscles. Her head turned slightly, eyes fixed on some distant object of desire.

"She's lovely," Daphne said, sitting on the steps that led from the garage into the kitchen. "*And* someone who you'll really connect with." She held a ceramic mug.

"I won't transport her nude, if that's what you're afraid of," Oscar said, giving Dora a clinical once-over. At the moment, she looked a little too mannequin-ish, too decorative. He needed to "human" her up.

"Is this gonna get creepy?" Daphne asked. "Is this a middle-aged crisis gone horribly wrong? I mean, I never looked like *that,* even at twenty."

And she didn't at fifty. Without any compelling reason to do otherwise, she had allowed herself over the decades to become shapeless and doughy around the hips. To compensate, she colored her hair black and indulged in sporadic raw vegetable purges. Oscar, at fifty-three, had managed to maintain the relatively poor shape he had acquired by thirty, getting neither better nor worse, and this he considered victory. His hair was sparse on the top, but he allowed it to grow in the back just past his collar. A narrow beard lined his jaw.

"I can only imagine the call from the police," she added, then shivered theatrically, gripping the mug.

"I repeat: this is a practical solution to a real problem. Nothing more."

"The cops will get you," Daphne said, standing up. "They always find people trying to game the system. You're no gamer." She headed back into the kitchen.

Oscar wore earplugs at the new job so that office small talk wouldn't distract him. He ate lunch in his cubicle and, in order to avoid the break room, brown-bagged items that wouldn't require refrigeration. His cubicle contained no personal clues. Work was for working, not showcasing photographs of the beach or art from eight-year-olds.

Daphne, however, did buy him an office plant, a cactus, with a note saying *Love and kisses, Dora.* It stuck out of the ceramic pot like a menacing cucumber. He placed it on the floor in the corner.

With nothing on display, no one asked questions unrelated to procedure. His work, as a result, was efficient. His boss told him as much on his initial one-month review.

"There is not a single thing wrong with a single thing you have done," said the boss, a tall, soft-spoken Dutchman with white hair neatly parted on the side. On his office wall was a series of nine watercolor paintings of small turtles, all together forming a kind of slide show. Oscar thought the turtles looked worried.

A coworker who shared his job title and who sat in the next cubicle was Bob Beasley. Upon meeting, Beasley shook his hand heartily and said, "Bob Beasley. It's a pleasure. My buddies call me *Beasley*." He pronounced his name exuberantly, as though calling to himself from afar.

Beasley was at least fifteen years younger than Oscar. Dense black hair covered his head like protective gear. His cubicle was lined with empty cans of diet root beer, and beside his monitor sat a huge framed photo of him and a plump redhead flanking two freckled kids on a hayride. Beasley's face brimmed with the desire to accommodate.

Oscar's lips cramped into a smile, and after a strained pause he said, "Pleased to meet you...*Beasley*," and from that point on did everything he could to avoid addressing his coworker by name. Once, when he couldn't get around it, he tried calling him "Robert."

Beasley stared at him incredulously and said, "Robert?" An admin named Celeste walked over and handed Beasley a stack of collated spreadsheets. "Here you are, *Robert*," she said and giggled. Celeste was a Filipino girl somewhere between the ages of twenty-five and forty. She took frequent cigarette breaks in the parking lot, had sparkling toenails, and liked to supplement her boobs with purple bras. "Ex*cuse* me," she said to Oscar, finger to her brow, "but my eyes are up *here*." Oscar immediately homed in on her forehead, staring intensely, his face a slab of expressionless stone. After a moment, he turned back to his cubicle.

"I always say that," he heard her say to Beasley as he reinserted his earplugs. "I always go to some creepy dude, *My eyes are up here*." She pronounced "always" *o-weez*.

Beasley, however, seemed to forget the whole thing and a few weeks later, on a Monday, brought in a small cooler of frozen trout, scaled and gutted, that he had caught over the weekend. He invited Oscar to check out his fishing photo album on Facebook (most people in the department were Facebook friends), then mentioned the name of the lake. Oscar knew it. The lake was only three miles from his house. Daphne's book group recently canoed there. Beasley handed his catch to Oscar and said, "Enjoy!"

Not only was Beasley a weekend outdoorsman who brought gifts to the office, but he was also Oscar's neighbor. Oscar didn't say a word.

Oscar had hoped to avoid the company holiday party, but was told by his boss that a number of clients would be dropping by, so everyone in their department was expected to attend. Caterers turned the lobby into a banquet hall with ethnic buffets stationed along the perimeter. A band played cocktail music on a makeshift stage just outside the HR suite.

He found himself in a not-painful conversation with three engineers from an electronics manufacturer. A teetotaler, Oscar sipped cream soda from a sleek, narrow Champagne glass while the engineers took turns ordering each other shots. One of them asked Oscar how to adjust a vibrating inkjet nozzle, and during the course of his answer, by way of illustration, Oscar let slip his passion for model trains. It turned out that five years earlier he and that engineer had attended the same model train convention in Lowell. They smiled and agreed that as one gets older, the world gets smaller.

Oscar's boss walked over holding a glass of white wine. He smiled gently at Oscar and, with his hand on the shoulder of one of the engineers, redirected the three of them to a new district manager, leaving Oscar alone with his cream soda. He looked at his watch and decided that in fifteen minutes he would have fulfilled his obligation, after which he (and Dora) could leave. He stood beside a tall, rubbery lobby plant and felt himself blend into the ambience. People stepped around him as though he were nothing more than a support beam. Even the wait staff, wiggling through the crowd distributing finger food, didn't realize he was fully human. As soon as the fifteen minutes expired, he set down the Champagne glass and loosened his tie when Celeste staggered up to him wearing a ruthlessly low-cut sequined dress. She had just stepped out from a small social cluster that included Beasley and his redheaded wife.

"Celeste, no!" someone called after her, but she turned and shushed them.

"Can I help you?" Oscar asked as Celeste brushed something off his shoulder, trying not to spill her beer. Her bra was as purple as a Japanese iris.

"Well," she said, catching her balance, "we all"—and she tossed a quick glance to her cluster, splashing her drink on her hand—"we all

were taking a vote"—she wiped her hand on her fish-netted thigh—
"seeing who in our department was most likely to, you know, *do* stuff
like, I dunno, get eaten by a bear—that's Beasley—or run off with Brad
Pitt—that's me. Adam got voted most likely to be mistaken for Clark
Kent. Keith got voted most likely to take over the company in a hot-
style takeover." She probably meant "hostile" takeover. "And *you,* my
dear"—she placed two fingers on his chest, right where his rib cage
cleaved—"you *also* got voted most likely to do something."

"Celeste!" someone pleaded. She waved dismissively, which again
caused her to spill a few drops. She licked her wrist, then said, "Wanna
know what?"

He did, but also didn't.

"Well," she continued, "since you're *clearly* at the edge of your seat,"
she swallowed hard, "we all of us unanimously voted *you,* Mr. Oscar
Clemente, most likely to get caught with a dead hooker in the trunk!"
And her lips popped in a bubble of wet laughter.

"I'm sorry," she said, backing away and holding her hand up inno-
cently as laughter consumed her body. The cluster reabsorbed her and
someone, Beasley?, exclaimed, "Oh you didn't!"

Oscar had no idea why they would have voted such a thing. He
hadn't seen a prostitute in nearly ten years, and when he did he was
cordial. Of course, *they* would have no way of knowing that.

He then concluded that Celeste was a stupid, ignorant person, and
that parties had a way of escalating ignorance and stupidity.

Yes, it was a good job, and he was lucky to have it. Coworkers were
a necessary evil. He put on his hat and left.

The commute worked beautifully. On good days, door to door, it took
an hour. Countless times he sailed down the HOV lane through Boston's central artery while the standard commuter lanes were gummed
up. He passed many police checkpoints, but he and Dora were never
flagged. This he owed to careful planning, especially after researching
how others had failed at this same ruse, often with police confiscating
the "passenger." Dora's hair was disheveled and rushed, and he never
hid her under a floppy sun hat. (For some reason, people always put
floppy sun hats on mannequins, even at night.) Fortunately, her face
turned slightly toward the driver's side, and whenever they approached
a police car, he began speaking to her angrily. But the real stroke of

genius, in his opinion, was the travel mug, whose handle wedged easily between her fingers and knee and which was visible from outside the car. She looked perfect.

Typically, he left his home in New Hampshire with Dora disassembled in the trunk. In Stoneham, just off I-93, he drove behind a gas station, parked, attached her torso to her waist, and dressed her. It took less than five minutes. After passing through Boston's central artery, he pulled into a vacant strip mall in downtown Quincy and put her back. Again, less than five minutes. Going home, he simply reversed the process.

But even the HOV lane wasn't perfect. Sometimes the backup was so severe that no one was spared. On one morning in January, Oscar had gotten a late start, and the traffic was merciless. He was jammed in Somerville, just north of Boston, and the HOV lane felt like a procession of the blind, cars thrust bumper-to-bumper straight into the sun's glare. Stupidly, he tried to wash the windshield, but the wipers smeared his view into a cataract of aerosolized light. He quickly grabbed a fistful of napkins from the glove box, stepped out of the car, and, with one hand guarding his necktie, scrubbed out a clear circle. The wind nearly blew his fedora off.

When he got back into the car, he said, "Where do they all come from?" Dora wore a long dark coat and a red cap. The shoulder strap held her torso in place, lifting her legs from the floor a few inches. It looked unnatural, but only from the inside. She stared out the windshield at the Boston skyline, focused on something imperceptible and distant.

Oscar, meanwhile, marveled at the sheer volume of people, an unrelenting torrent that seemed to have no beginning or end.

"It is like those pornographic films you can now watch on your computer," he said. "The young women who do this sort of thing, they're endless. You can watch thousands of these short films and never see the same young woman twice. Where do they all come from? Is there someplace where they hatch, fully formed? Do they just come up out of the ground after it's rained? Ha ha!"

He didn't feel it was odd to talk to her, because really, he was talking to himself. Most conversations, when you got right down to it, were little more than listening to someone else think out loud while you waited your turn.

He thought about this for a moment, then said, "Chitchat, the kind that goes on at the water cooler, is just a way to showcase your own internal monologue."

He liked this insight.

"Conversation," he continued, "is just a way to talk to yourself without feeling peculiar."

He glanced at her, admiring her poise.

"I'm sure you'd agree if you could."

She held her travel mug.

"Really," he said, tapping the steering wheel, "when you get right down to it, what *is* there to really say?"

She didn't say.

"Or *hear*, for that matter?"

She didn't do that either.

He sighed loudly, with drama. "Where do they all come from?"

On Thursday nights and Saturday mornings Daphne attended rehearsals for a local theater group. It was a small, volunteer company, and she designed costumes and played small bit parts once in a while. When she and Oscar first met in graduate school, he expressed a cautious interest in theater. He had gone so far as to audition for the role of the Ghost in *Hamlet*, but ended up as a mourner at Ophelia's funeral. He wasn't bad, but as Daphne's interest in drama was piqued, he focused all the more on his various internships, soon landing an entry-level position at an aerospace manufacturer.

With neither expecting too much from the other, Oscar and Daphne coexisted easily, each pursuing their passions separately—hers being theater and book groups and a host of volunteering opportunities; his being model trains, as well as the development of processes and systems.

But as the years passed, what had once been a small weakness of Oscar's grew into something beyond his control: While he had always been a person who sought solitude, over the years, increasingly, Oscar could only be alone when Daphne was in the house. Poking about in the basement or the study was best with intermittent interruptions, such as the toilet flushing somewhere upstairs or reminders to transfer funds or get the oil changed. He relished having the whole house to himself, but only when he knew she'd be back in a few hours to ruin it. Three years ago, after her father's kidney transplant, she flew back to Indiana for two weeks to help her parents out. The entire time she was gone, Oscar barely slept, barely got anything done. Simply feeding himself required advanced planning. When she returned, he was so confused by the mix of rage and relief that he locked himself in the basement for an entire Sunday soldering metal objects.

Which was why he couldn't take his eyes off her when she announced she would be gone for five days with her theater group in Pennsylvania the following week. The news caused electric prickles to spill down his thighs.

"Of course," she said, slaughtering carrots in a juicer, "significant others are welcome. Toby's wife Marisa's gonna tweet it." Vegetable roughage lined the sink.

The thought of being confined with these people in a motel pressed down on his chest. "I'm not sure if I've accrued enough time off," he said between breaths.

"Oscar, are you going to start getting all funky on me again? Look, as fun as it would be to have you come along and not talk to anyone, stay back here. You and Dora can have the place all to yourselves." She bit a chunk of celery and offered him the remaining stalk.

The first night he did OK. He came home from work and, with Dora safely in the trunk, spent most of the evening in the basement with his model trains, pizza, and a few cans of cream soda. He convinced himself he should forget that Daphne wasn't there. When his head hit the pillow at 1:00 a.m., he instantly fell asleep. The following day, though, he was edgy and even removed his earplugs and stared unblinking at a coworker who laughed too loud. He didn't eat, and that night he didn't sleep, and the following morning he felt ill.

"You OK there, O-man?" Beasley asked. Beasley had nicknames for everyone, and Oscar had decided that letting him get away with O-man was the least of his worries—even though he once heard someone repeat "Omen." An Indian fellow kept calling him "Ooo-mahn." Once, at a meeting, Celeste didn't see that Oscar was there and asked, "Where's O-*scary?*"

"I'm fine, thank you," Oscar answered Beasley, feeling wet inside his undershirt. By 3:00 p.m. he knew he had a fever, but all he could find in the office First Aid kit were tweezers and antibiotic goo in a tube.

Daphne called him at 4:30 to remind him about a dentist appointment, and Oscar whispered into the phone, "You have to come get me. I can't drive."

"Oscar, I'm in Altoona."

Of course she was. He'd forgotten.

"Oscar, why don't you call the doctor? Or have a coworker drive you home. Who's that man in our town?"

"Robert Beasley," he whispered, his hand cupping the receiver. "And I won't. Can you come back?"

"Oscar, I'm seven hours away. Remember? Pennsylvania? Look, do you need to go to an ER?"

Oscar rested his face against the phone as his elbow sunk into the armrest. He closed his eyes. Immediately he heard a faint *whoosh* deep inside his ears. He felt himself levitate, ever so slightly, and the *whoosh* tensed into a tight, keen ring. The phone hit the floor and he quickly shot up in his chair. He picked it up and said, "Dora?" but was answered by the dial tone. He stood and then sat right down after almost falling on the cactus. Once the dizziness passed, he went to the bathroom. Without dropping his trousers he sat on a toilet.

"O-man," Beasley said a few minutes later, over by the urinals. "Since when the heck do you live in Derry? All this time and you never said? What the frig!" He flushed. "Soooo, your wife calls and says you need a lift, and I don't blame her. I was thinking before you look like something I'd fish out of a pond. Ha!" He ran water and then yanked out a few paper towels. Oscar's head drooped. "I car-pooled here today, so I'm happy to drive you home. What say you?" Beasley tapped gently on the stall door. Because Oscar had forgotten to latch it, the door drifted open. "Oops" said Beasley.

Oscar looked up and squinted at Beasley's head, at his impenetrable hair gleaming in the cold fluorescence. Beasley had an expression that Oscar had witnessed countless times yet always found puzzling, a look where the mouth mimics a smile while the eyes dampen with worry. You saw it a lot with HR reps and therapists; superiority feigning modesty. But Oscar, blood burning and skin freezing, had no way to defend himself. He reached into his trousers and offered the dangling keys.

In the parking garage, he waved at the Camry.

"No, thank you," he said when Beasley offered to help him into the passenger seat. "You really don't need to do this," he said as the car entered I-93 north. But really, he did. Oscar, cocooned in his coat, blasted the heat, shivering inside his own sweat. Beasley chuckled and explained how this was nothing, and how he was happy to oblige, and how he wished he could do stuff like this more often. During the ride, he asked Oscar lots of questions, volunteering his own answers when it became clear that Oscar wasn't talking.

"So how long's it take you door to door? Probably over an hour. On a good day I can do it in an hour. You like living up in Derry? Bet you do, if you're willing to work all the way down here. You go fishing? Camping? Why the hell would you live in New Hampshire if you didn't! Hey, you hear about that new species of cat they discovered in Borneo? Seriously!" And on it went. Eventually, around the state line, Beasley's voice, the road, the blasting heat, it all converged.

Oscar dozed, soothed by the vibrations of the headrest against his neck. He began dreaming a series of detached images and bodiless voices. There was no continuity, just fevered threads unified by unease. Daphne, from somewhere far off, warned him about all sorts of stuff that he couldn't quite follow. Dora, beside him in the passenger seat, gazed at a cluster of bruised clouds. Wait, no—that wasn't right. Dora was in the trunk. He knew this because he could hear her detached leg kick against the trunk's interior. There was a rhythm to her kicking, and Oscar could feel it pulsing against the headrest. It must have been difficult for her, being a body but also something less than a body. Maybe that was why she kicked so hard.

Oscar woke to the creak of the trunk popping. The Camry idled at the side of the highway, cars rocketing past, as Beasley, outside, made his way to the rear. A bolt of adrenaline pushed Oscar from his seat. He toppled out the passenger side, intercepting Beasley and slamming the trunk, but not before they both got a clear look at Dora's face. She was nestled against her own legs, gazing dreamily at them.

Oscar panted and he pressed the trunk down. Beasley stood there in his parka, arms hanging.

"We got a flat," he said weakly. "I was just gonna change the flat."

Oscar struggled for breath. "Get back in the car," he panted.

"The tire blew," Beasley said. "I was just gonna change…What's in your trunk? There's a doll in your trunk?"

The adrenaline bolt gave Oscar an illusion of instant health. "Get back in the car," he said. "*I'll* change the flat."

Beasley protested, but without any force. After a few weak attempts, he returned to the car and sat down in the passenger side. Oscar slid Dora to the back of the trunk and removed the tire and lug wrench. He pointed the wrench at Beasley and ordered him to stay put, then jacked up the rear. He changed the tire quickly, before his knuckles and ears went numb, before the chemical rush dissolved and his fever reasserted itself. He spread the plaid pantsuit over Dora's limbs and got back into the car—cold, sweaty, nauseous. Despite this, he drove.

Beasley slouched in his seat, looking small in his jacket. "You gonna make it?" he asked in a voice that had lost all confidence.

But they were barely ten miles from Derry, and Oscar was certain he had at least that much left in him. "Just tell me where you live," he said.

They made it to Beasley's house in twenty minutes. Aside from an occasional "You *sure* you're OK?" the ride was silent.

Beasley got out and asked if that *thing* in the trunk was one of those *things* Japanese guys use, and Oscar croaked no and quickly drove off, expecting to pull over and puke at any point. But he didn't. By the time he made it into his garage he actually wondered if he might die. He swallowed a few Advils and collapsed on the couch, shivering inside a comforter as he stared at a news program.

Within an hour the fever had noticeably dropped. Daphne called the home phone and, after berating Oscar for not answering his cell, told him to make sure he thanked Beasley and cancelled the dentist, in that order. Oscar hung up while she was still talking and got into bed. It was dark and it felt late, but once again he couldn't sleep. He was deathly tired and the Advil had relieved the chills and the aches, but a restlessness raced through him, one that made him acutely aware of each beat of his heart. He couldn't stop replaying the indecent horror of Beasley gawking at Dora.

Daphne wouldn't be home for two more nights, but two nights might as well have been twenty. After what felt like hours, he made his way into the garage and popped the trunk.

Oscar was wearing a sweat suit and wool socks, but the garage, unheated, plunged him into a sickly chill. As fast as he could, in two trips, he carried her into the house, leaving her clothes behind. He shivered as he assembled her, quickly wrapping the both of them up beneath the bed sheets. He pulled her close.

She was cold and her elbow jabbed his hip. He spooned her, which was easy since her knees were permanently bent. His arm reached naturally across her stomach. But the arch of her spine didn't feel right, and he wished her legs weren't so tightly crossed. He tried a few times to accommodate her posture, but this only frustrated him more.

Finally, he got out of bed and looked through the bathroom cabinet for allergy medication, anything to knock him out. With no luck, he turned to the linen closet. As he shuffled through hand towels and Q-tips and cotton balls, Oscar found a pink bottle of Hawaiian Tropic sunblock. He took it out and held it up to the hallway light. On the back was a silhouette of a woman reclining. Her hair reached the sand. He held the container tightly. The plastic was warm. He smelled the inside of the cap, and the smell of warm summer skin tingled up his nose, deep into his sinuses. He took the bottle back to the bedroom and applied lotion to Dora's shoulders. He knew this was odd, but whatever. He hadn't touched anyone this way in ages. He tried massaging the cream evenly but ended up smearing the bed sheet. Of course, nothing was absorbed, and no matter how widely he dispersed the lotion up her neck and down her back and arms, the white streaks remained. *Idiot,* he said to himself. *What did you think would happen?* It took almost half a box of tissues to remove the product, but when he finally turned off the light and lay down, the room blossomed with smells of summer. He closed his eyes and breathed through his nose, smelling the warm sky, the ocean, all those glimmering blues and greens. He moved closer to her, smelling her neck through her hair. He was flush with the thrill of youthful memories, like mothers tanning at community pools, boys kissing girls in flip-flops, and teeming, humid nights. He breathed deep, and slow, feeling this strange and achy beauty float just out of reach.

Outside, the February wind shook the windows. But here, under covers, Dora was abundant.

Oscar was out of work for two days, but when he returned, things were different. For starters, no one called him O-man or Omen anymore. Just Oscar. What's more, they really didn't even call him Oscar. They didn't call him anything. They didn't even *call* him. Beasley, who sat in the adjoining cubicle, e-mailed when he had a question. Everyone spoke to him electronically now, and when they couldn't help but address him in person, they never made eye contact. One morning, he opened up his desk drawer and found a white piece of paper with letters clipped from a magazine spelling out "CREEPY." He smelled the paper and sensed a lingering trace of the perfume he pictured Celeste dabbling on her chest. He slammed the drawer. Around him the office hummed with concentration.

His boss called him in.

"Oscar, is everything all right?" The boss spoke gently, but his face lacked any hint of concern.

"Yes, fine," Oscar said, gazing at the beleaguered turtles.

"Are you sure?"

"Everything's fine."

His boss stared at him a good long time before finally asking, "Are you sure everything is OK?"

"Yes, thank you." Eventually, the phone rang and Oscar left.

"I feel as though things are winding down for me," Oscar explained to Dora as they drove home. "It's that feeling in the air."

Up ahead, as the highway curved between two hills, he caught the last glimmer of sunset, the burn-off in the trees turning a darkened blue. This was the first inkling that the days were getting longer. He glanced at Dora and noted that the coffee mug in her hand was about to fall. He reached over and wedged it back in place, skewing her posture.

"Sorry," he muttered.

Ever since their one night together, he found it hard to relax around her. Conversation felt stilted. For the first time in months he wondered if he might prefer commuting alone. Of course, he never said this aloud.

"I'm sure I'll get something else if this doesn't pan out," he said. "I'm a man of remarkable skills. Maybe even something closer to home." He didn't look at her after he said this. She stared off into the distance, looking to where the sunset had been.

That night, he went to see the final production of Daphne's play, the very one she had abandoned him for not long ago. He sat in the back row of the local community center's main function room, flanked by two teenagers who poked him with bony elbows as they texted.

He had trouble following the play, which was a mash-up of traditional Slavic folk tales. The performers danced to music played on wooden instruments. Some of the dances required the cast to spread out through the auditorium. Daphne had apparently costumed the players in their brightly colored peasant garments. A blond woman danced across the stage in a floral robe—the goddess of spring—joyously tossing white flowers into the audience from a wicker basket, and it wasn't until she recited a rhyming couplet that Oscar realized it was Daphne. She looked so real inside her wig, so alive, and Oscar, contracting himself from the grazing elbows, wondered for one quick second if going with her to Altoona would have been less hellish than being alone.

Oscar's boss's admin poked her head in his cubicle and asked, "Got a sec?" and led him to the corner office.

Sitting across from the boss was a woman in a tan suit he vaguely recognized and who introduced herself as a human resources associate. She had spiky gray hair and shadowy eye makeup. She explained to him how the company was currently streamlining efficiencies and thus consolidating his position into another's portfolio.

"Whose?" he asked.

"Bob Beasley's," said his boss, fiddling with a paperclip. The woman went on to explain how since he had been there less than a year, they weren't obligated to pay severance, but because they felt terrible about this, they were giving him one month's pay. She handed him his check and explained his options regarding benefits. She also said, apologetically, that IT was currently removing his access to e-mail and the shared drive, but that he shouldn't take this personally. If any of this was too hard to remember—and she could understand why it might be—it was all made perfectly clear in the documents enclosed in the large white envelope she offered.

"I see," he said, but didn't.

Back at his cubicle a young, black security guard with pony-tailed dreadlocks held a cardboard box, "for your personal belongings," and Oscar, his face a slab of expressionless stone, piled random things inside and grabbed his coat.

"Geez, Oscar, I'm so sorry," he heard Beasley say as the security guard led him through the exit to the parking garage. He heard others following behind but didn't turn. He glanced down and realized that the small stack of things in his box was topped with CREEPY.

His car was two spaces from the exit, and he immediately felt the cold against his head and realized that in his haste he had forgotten his hat. He turned, and there at the glass doors stood Beasley holding the cactus with both hands. He bore that same look—smiling mouth and worried eyes—that had puzzled Oscar weeks earlier. Beside Beasley stood the boss, holding the large, white HR envelope, which Oscar had also forgotten in the confusion. Celeste tagged along, because stuff like this was too good to miss. The security guard wished he were anyplace but here. Oscar handed him the box and removed his keys from his pocket.

"You're all just dying to see, aren't you," he said. This stopped them in their tracks. Celeste stood on tiptoes to peek over Beasley's shoulder. "Well then, come on."

Before the boss could take control, Oscar popped the trunk.

Dora's torso was laid out perfectly for a viewing. She faced them as they gathered, staring beyond the small crowd and off into the distance. Her bottom half fitted snugly beside her so that her feet tucked against where her waist would normally be.

"I believe she's been the source of—" he wanted to conclude the sentence with "a misunderstanding," and then underscore how this was nothing more than a practical solution to a real problem, and how she had never been anything other than that. But words swelled in his throat. Dora, clearly, had no idea she was as good as dead. Even in a trunk, even in pieces, she continued to gaze at that remote object of desire, that single elusive thing that always pulled her away from wherever she was.

BRUCE COHEN
Curious Questions

I am successfully cupping fireflies with my make believe hand.
I am admiring the invisible irises I forgot to plant last November.
I actually see the tie-dye evolution of autumn leaves for the first time

My son said after we left the hospice where my mother would be
A ghost before we ever saw her again. A Candy Stripe girl blurted out
That art, to her, was liquid curiosity & who could dispute that?

We seep out of ourselves or outgrow ourselves. Two theories: the shirt
Shrunk in the dryer or our make believe arms continue to reach
     beyond.
Yes, there are complete sentences comprised solely of punctuation!

It's sort of sad to stand with my unsanitized plastic basket in the
     express
Line after having to reshelve a couple of vital ingredients to slip
     under the 13
Item radar. Although we are trusted to self monitor my mother
     lambasted

Me for having 14 but I thought peanut butter & jelly, like Siamese
     twins,
Counted as one. Sometimes the entire shopper population seems
     composed
Of bachelors & widows & those scooting around in electric carts.
     I think

The dead can hear our thinking so I try to temper mine to less than
     13 thoughts.
Though I'm not a cannibal but a man with a complicated sweet tooth
     I want
To bite the sugary heads off the bride & groom replicas on top of
     wedding cakes

Before the brides & grooms do. If they can make trick candles you
    can't blow out
Why can't they invent ones that burn indefinitely? Soon, I suppose,
    we'll be able
To take our cell phones & press them to our ears & our brains will
    absorb the data.

What part of speech is download? No more talking: two people
    simply touch heads—
We kiss each other from a hundred miles away, someday, one
    wordless complete
Sentence with definite pronouns. I am catching make believe fireflies
    in my real hand.

I am thinking about the time I hadn't even crossed the border
But I thought I had versus the time I crossed the border & didn't
    realize it.
I want to be a contestant on Jeopardy but am geographically ignorant

& I flunked entomology: bug-study, not words. I mean is that the
    right word
Or is it etymology? I get mixed up! Questions should be reserved for
    ignorance.
I stare at the hospital made bed where my mother was & I find the
    evolutionary

Biology of fireflies to be most amazing, how they reveal briefly
Their whereabouts & more often than not, entice one, in their teasing
Disappearance, to grab that elusive darkness within the darkness.

TADEUSZ DĄBROWSKI

"I tried to save as many of them..."

Translated by Antonia Lloyd-Jones

I tried to save as many of them as possible from the fire
of impressions, from the ship going to the bottom
of memory, where the guard is kept by electric
fishes. Most were asleep, so the dying lasted
as long as a breath. This was my battle for continuity,
but I scattered like a sentence on a child's lips
laid over and over in the grave, like a firework
into a thousand sparks, which cannot be put together
not even as a damp squib. I go up to myself, freckle-faced
in a little captain's uniform, up to a teenager with
an instant camera, hunting after ravens,
up to myself writing this poem. I see each of them,
but they fail to recognize me. Or maybe they're simply
afraid of death.

SIERRA GOLDEN
The Sound of Oars

> *To hear the faint sound of oars in the silence as a rowboat*
> *comes slowly out and then goes back is truly worth*
> *all the years of sorrow that are to come.*
>   —Jack Gilbert, "A Brief for the Defense"

I'm here, listening to the sound of oars
dipping and dripping while they pull across the sound,
and, it's true, I'm enjoying my life. At times, I've almost forgotten
the faces of suffering, the flies, but this is not what God wants.
Look, even here, the sheen of oil, a radiant rainbow scar,
and the scent of bleach hovering above a fish creek.
It's the same everywhere: sorrow and slaughter,
the world burning with hopelessness and violence.
Tonight I stand on the bow of a small boat, moored in a tiny port,
the town three shuttered cafés and a bar, shouting and music.
In the morning while sea otters slap through the kelp, feeding,
someone wakes in the street, the neighborhood's curtains clamped
shut. Nobody escapes, but you say *to make injustice*
the only measure of our attention is to praise the Devil.
What then? Your stubborn delight is not enough either,
even the rockfish migrate, rising from darkness at sunrise,
sinking again in the night.

MARY GORDON
What Remains

It was too late when I was called in, but it was probably always too late, which is to say there was really never any hope. People didn't want to believe that—even some of the people who were closest to Beth, maybe them most of all. They would ask me for a long time after Rowena died if Beth was wrong for staying with the homeopath for so long, nearly three months after Rowena first got sick. I told them she'd done nothing wrong, that no one could have done anything. They thought I had an answer for something unanswerable, a comprehension of something incomprehensible. Perhaps it was because I was a doctor, perhaps it was because I was a good ten years older than them, perhaps because my family had lived in the town for generations and most of them were late arrivals, settling into our little town in the Berkshires in the late sixties. So they kept talking to me about Rowena's death and I knew why. They wanted me to say it didn't have to happen, that it could have been prevented if someone had been smarter, more vigilant, better informed. When something unbearable happens—and what is more unbearable than the death of a child—people want to think there was something that could have been done to prevent it. It's the only way they can feel safe. But nothing could have prevented the death of Rowena Carmichael at the age of five. Or I suppose there could have been a miracle. But a miracle did not occur.

Beth had first come to our part of the world as part of a modern dance troupe that performed one summer at Jacob's Pillow. It was sometime in the '70s, maybe '73 or '74. I don't know quite how Roland got here, I never knew him very well. To tell the truth, he never interested me that much. Everyone knew Beth was much more interesting.

For one thing, she was fascinating-looking. When I first knew her, she was only in her twenties, but her hair had gone quite gray. She had the most remarkable hair. It wasn't gray, really, that's misleading, to say it was gray; it was more like silver, like a source of light. Once when I was watching her walk down the street, I thought of her hair as a sheaf of moonlight.

Most of the other young mothers in town had long hair, but she had cut hers so it fell just below her ears, perfectly straight like a kind of soft helmet. You could always spot her from far away.

She gave dance classes for children in the basement of the Congregational Church. Roland worked in the health food store and did some carpentry. I always supposed they had some sort of family money. In those days, young couples seemed to be able to live on very little money. Nobody seems to be able to live on very little money now.

They had only one child, a little girl, Rowena. Rowena's hair was straight and thick and dark, jet black, an unusual texture and color for a child. I supposed that Beth's hair had been like that before it turned.

I don't think I'd ever talked to any of them before they brought Rowena to my office. We didn't travel in the same circles; I didn't go to the health food store, and my children were boys and too old for Beth's dance classes anyway. Beth was the kind of woman who just irritated my wife; Lois wanted people to be one thing or another, either conventional wives and mothers or driven career women. "All these long skirts and beads and patchouli," she'd say, giving an exaggerated shudder.

Beth and Roland had never come to the office before; they were of the group that didn't believe in vaccines and preferred herbs to antibiotics.

But they were in my office that day because Rowena had had a seizure. She'd been having dizzy spells and headaches, but they were getting worse, and Beth believed now that the homeopath was "out of her depth." But I was out of my depth too. I sent them to a pediatric neurologist at Mass General. But I knew it was hopeless.

I was surprised when she made another appointment. She said I was the only one of all the doctors she'd spoken to who acted like a human being. She'd been given two different options and she wanted my opinion. One neurologist suggested surgery; two others had said the operation would do no good, that the best thing would be to keep her as comfortable as possible.

"What do you think? Do you think I should just try everything so afterward I don't blame myself for not trying enough?"

I told her that I really wasn't qualified to choose between two opinions that had been offered by people far more expert than I, but that whatever she decided, I would do everything I could to help.

"My child is probably going to die and I don't know what to do about it," she said. Her eyes were glassy; I wasn't sure she even knew I was there. So I was silent.

"I like that you don't say anything when you don't know what to say," she said.

"You can say anything you like to me, anytime you need to," I said.

"Yes, she said. "Yes, I know."

She decided on the surgery, but it wasn't a success. Rowena died three weeks later. She was in our local hospital. At least I was able to insist that Beth be allowed to stay with her all the time, that they set up a cot next to Rowena's bed so she could be there. When I think of that time, I don't remember anything about Roland. Only Beth, sitting beside her dying child, with her remarkable hair. And her lovely complexion, which always reminded you of the sun. In all weathers, and even under the harsh hospital lights, it made you think of early roses.

But it wasn't in my caring for Rowena in her last days or my care of Beth afterward as her doctor that I played my most important role. The important part happened seven years after Rowena's death.

I guess I was a help in the time just after Rowena died. I signed the death certificate. I was there at the burial. Somehow Beth had got around whatever laws there were: Rowena was buried on their land, unembalmed. Beth had made a shroud for her dead child; the cloth was very beautiful, blue shot silk, with threads of gold. Roland dug the grave and Beth laid the shroud with the dead body into it. Roland covered it with dirt and then played a song on his harmonica. "Going Home," it was called. I knew that it was the song that had accompanied FDR's funeral train in its progress across the country, and I guessed that I was the only one old enough to have remembered that.

And I was the one who told Beth, only a year after Rowena's death, that she'd gone into early menopause. She had come into the office complaining of night sweats and missed periods. She was only thirty-one, and I explained to her that early menopause could sometimes be brought about by great stress. And, of course, she had experienced a stress that was nearly unimaginable.

I didn't see her much after that. She came in once for me to take a look at a rash; it turned out to be impetigo. And one year, she gave in when she'd had a cough that didn't go away for three months; I diagnosed bronchitis; she reluctantly agreed to amoxicillin. I was hoping there was nothing seriously wrong when I saw her name in my appointment book one day in August, seven years after Rowena's death."

She sat across the desk from me, her brilliant hair reminding me more than ever of the moon because of the crescent shape it made as it brushed her chin.

"I'll get right to the point" she said, and I could see in her eyes and hear in her voice the habit of certainty, of purpose, someone used to command and control.

"I'm not here to consult you as a doctor, at least not in the ordinary way. I have an enormous favor to ask of you. An outrageous favor, really."

I tried to imagine what it might be. Did she want me to prescribe a lethal dose of morphine to speed up the death of a mother or father? Was the early menopause a false alarm? Did she want me to perform a late-term abortion? Provide her with a regular supply of amphetamines and barbiturates? When patients asked me for a favor, it was so often connected with a desire for oblivion; they wanted me to facilitate a smaller or a greater death.

What she told me was almost unbelievable. Someone had bought the field next to Beth and Roland's property. A developer. It was the beginning of what would become a trend: cheap houses that seemed to be sold by the pound, each one imitating something, none of them with the clarity and simplicity of our vernacular architecture. When the developers bought the land, it had to be resurveyed, and it was discovered that the boundary lines of the property had changed. Rowena's grave was no longer on the Carmichaels' property. Now it would be abutting someone's barbecue or basketball hoop or oversize garage.

"You see, it wasn't exactly legal for us to bury her on our property... not the way we did. I never went through the bureaucratic hoops, and I guess I just got away with it because people felt bad for me after Rowena's death. But now they've come down on me like a ton of bricks; they won't budge."

"That's terrible," I said. "It must be stopped."

"I'm afraid it can't be...I haven't a leg to stand on. And even if the boundaries were redrawn a bit, she'd still be close to strangers. I've come to understand that she'll have to be disinterred and reburied, closer to our house. There's no other way. And that's the favor I need to ask of you. Roland wants to do it himself. But I told him this is something he simply must not do."

Her silver hair was never more like a helmet than at that moment, but where I'd seen a soft helmet of silkiness, I now saw cold, hard metal. And the rosy undertone that had always seemed to me a sign of a deep inner tenderness was now a feverish color: it suggested flame rather than roses.

"My husband doesn't understand. He doesn't understand anything. What the dead are. Who they are. What death means. He doesn't understand that there are some things that absolutely must not be seen. Must not be looked at. Because their power is so great, it will drive out everything else. Everything else that is real and true. Everything that makes life bearable. It is unbearable to lose a child. One bears it by calling up memories of the healthy child. Scenes, images of beauty and freshness. And those would be impossible if what was burned into the eyes, the mind, was a skeleton or some sort of grotesque combination of bone and intact flesh. That the darling face, the soft, sweet cheeks are now a skull: that must not be seen; it must not be remembered. Then you could only think: This is what death is. This is what my child is. And that could not be borne. But he doesn't understand that. He doesn't understand anything."

She was leaning so far forward in her chair that I was afraid she was going to leap at me: put her hands around my throat and threaten me if I didn't do what she said. But I had no impulse not to do it. I was nearly awestruck by her words: by their clarity, their courage.

"What does Roland want?" I asked, taking courage from her courage.

"It doesn't matter what he wants. He has no understanding."

The brightness had drained from her eyes, as if it had been leached and then absorbed into that wonderful hair, which gleamed now, took on sharpness. I could only think of a knife's sharpness, or the killing blade of a sword. The cold, the sharpness of her was thrilling and terrible. Who could live with that clarity? And the light that shone from that clarity could only fall on those in shadow with a pure contempt that would be devastating, deathly.

I felt sorry for Roland, whom I knew was the victim of that contempt. But I knew Beth was right, and I knew that I must take my place beside her greatness.

"I need you to do this for me, John," she said. "There's no one else who could possibly do it. You have experience with death, with the bodies of the dead. And you are kind and truthful. Will you do this for me, John? Please tell me I can rely on you."

I wanted to tell her that I had no experience with anything like this, that I dealt with the bodies of the living. Then I remembered that I had, in medical school, dissected a cadaver, and I thought that she might know that and bring it up if I said I had no experience with the bodies of the dead. And so, of course, I had to agree. I said I would work out the details within a day or two. But she could count on me.

I knew that I at least needed more information: I needed to know what I might be uncovering. I called a friend of mine, an old medical-school pal, who was a medical examiner now in Hartford. I asked him what were the possible fates of an unembalmed body, buried only in a silk shroud, after six years. He said that there were many factors that would contribute to the rate of decomposition. The soil's moisture. The presence of animals. He said I might be seeing anything from separate bones to a skeleton covered by partial musculature, even part of a face, he said. Or there might be nothing; the work of animals and moisture might mean that I would find no remains distinguishable from the ordinary soil.

I made a date with Beth, and she said she would bring the new shroud to the office the day before. She asked if I would do the reburial; Roland would dig the new grave. "Upper body strength is his long suit," she said, in a tone that shocked me. She said that when the reburial was done, she and Roland would have their own private ceremony. She said I must not tell her what I found in the grave. Of course, I could do nothing but agree.

It was a gentle, bluish gray May morning. I parked my car at the far end of Beth's property and walked toward the grave site, carrying my spade, whose edge I'd honed so it would be its most effective, and the new shroud she had made. The old one, I remembered, had been blue; this one was silvery, almost no color at all. The loud birdsong seemed both comforting and sacrilegious. I asked myself if I would have preferred total silence. Then I willed my mind to empty itself. What I was doing simply had to be done.

It was hard work, though I was young then and still in good shape.

But then the soil was light and loamy and it was easier than it might have been. I kept digging, deeper and deeper, but no matter how hard I dug, I didn't find anything but soil. I remembered what my friend the medical examiner had told me, that it was possible that the decay might be complete, that with the right conditions nothing might be left. But I thought it would be terrible if I had misjudged the depth and left something behind. After a while, though, I had to understand that what was left of Rowena was exactly nothing. And that seemed the worst possible thing to me, worse even than finding a grinning skull and delicate child's bones. What I kept thinking was: what if the dead are nothing. What if there's nothing we can go back to? Nothing that would mark the unique passing of an individual life. Nothing that remains.

And what would I put in the beautiful shroud Beth had sewn?

In the end, I shoveled a bit of dirt into the shroud and tied it up with the silk ribbons Beth had put at the bottom. I laid it in the grave Roland had dug, and covered it with earth. And then I drove away. From the car window, I saw Beth at her door. She raised her hand and waved. I waved back. And we never spoke of it again.

I wasn't at all surprised to hear that she and Roland were divorcing. I thought of the coldness of her words, "He understands nothing," and I knew that such contempt must mark the end of love. I was sorry she left town without saying goodbye. No one I spoke to seemed to know where she'd gone.

That was twenty years ago. And today, as if there were nothing strange about it, she appeared in my office, apologizing for not making an appointment. As if that were the important thing.

"I'm Beth," she said. "Beth Carmichael I was then, now I'm Beth Saramango."

Had I imagined that she wouldn't age? It had been twenty years, and she of course looked older. She was a beautiful woman still, but the quality of her beauty was so utterly different from what it had been that I would never have recognized her. I remembered the transformation I had seen. She'd turned into a knife blade, a sword's edge before my eyes. But more transformations had occurred. She had always been slender, but now she was pencil thin. The way she dressed accentuated her thinness; she was all in black, well-tailored black pants, high-heeled pointy black boots, a black shirt. Around her neck she wore a crimson scarf: like a slash across her throat. The moonlit silveriness that I had likened to a sheaf of light had turned to iron now. She wore her hair pulled tight into a neat bun: it was held by a silver clip, whose pattern I couldn't quite make out.

She looked all wrong in my office, foreign, even dangerous, like a sharp-beaked bird of striking coloration that had wandered into a meadow of dun-colored natives. I tried to decide if I was glad to see her. I had been sorry not to say goodbye, but I didn't want to remember that day, remember what I'd seen. What I'd seen should not be remembered, what I'd seen was what was not there. I had mostly forgotten it, and I realized how grateful I was for the years of forgetfulness. After the initial seconds of pleasure at the sight of a lovely woman, I felt her presence as a thief.

"I've been in Buenos Aires all this time," she said. "I guess it's twenty years. My life is all about the tango."

She must have seen that I was puzzled, because she laughed. Her laugh did soften the sharp features.

"I guess you find that strange, but I assure you in BA it's quite common.

I didn't know what she meant when she said BA. I thought she meant BO, an archaic abbreviation for body odor. Luckily, I caught on before I said anything mortifyingly stupid.

"I suppose you wonder why I'm here," she said.

I told her that I did wonder, but it was nice to see her.

She explained that she had sold the house when she and Roland had divorced, but had held on to the property. Knowing that Rowena was buried there, she wanted to be sure the grave would be undisturbed. But now, she said, she realized that Buenos Aires was really her home. After all these years, she had remarried and she was going to use the money she got for selling the land to open her own dance studio, one geared particularly to Americans wanting to learn tango.

"I felt very strange coming to see you," she said. "I've often thought that I asked you to do something terrible, and I see now that I had no right to do it. I excuse myself that, even years after Rowena's death, I was still in shock. Well, I'm not in shock now, John, and I'm not quite the wild hippie girl that I was. I've arranged with a mortician to have Rowena's remains disinterred. Whatever is left will be cremated. Do you know what they call the ashes after a cremation? Cremains, they're called. Isn't it awful? It sounds like some kind of high-fiber snack food. I just hate it."

Her words relieved me; for a moment I was afraid she was going to ask me to go into the child's grave again. And I was concerned that the undertaker would tell her there was nothing to cremate. But her next words shattered my relief.

"I'm going to ask you another favor," she said. "It's not so gruesome as the last. I just need your advice. You see, I'll have Rowena's ashes now; I'll have them with me. But before I get on the plane, I have to decide what to do with them. Should I scatter them here, here in the Berkshires, the only place she ever knew, or should I take them with me and rebury them in Buenos Aires, perhaps buy a plot for myself down there? You see, it's two different ways of dealing with her death. Do I just let it go, into the wind, into the air, or do I say: this is who I am. I am the mother of a dead child, and I will carry this into whatever eternity there is. What do you think, John, what would you do?"

Her eyes were shining; a thin film of tears covered them, but not enough so that the tears really fell. They weren't the cold eyes that I saw when she said her husband had no understanding, but there was something unalive about them, and she was not a woman I would like to have held in my arms. Not anymore.

I guess one of the privileges of being old is that you are allowed to say there are some things you will not do. And so I told her I had no idea what she should do, that I really didn't know her very well, and that it was a very intimate question and she should ask someone who knew her more intimately.

"Of course, you're exactly right," she said, standing up, as if she were a pupil dismissed by a punishing schoolmaster. Above all, I hadn't wanted to sound punishing, so I thought of asking her to sit down, to stay awhile.

But, in fact I didn't.

"It's very nice to see you John," she said. "Best of luck. You're a good man. Maybe a dying breed."

I deal with the sick and dying all the time, but more than any of those experiences, her words made me aware of my own mortality. That it would be coming sooner rather than later. That I would soon be more like the long-dead Rowena than like any of the living.

"It's nice to see you too, Beth," I said, knowing that I lied. Certainly she was nice to look at; even in her new incarnation, she was a lovely woman. But I wished she hadn't come. I wished I didn't have to look at her again. Because even though I'd refused the task she'd set for me, the task of helping her decide, she'd set me a new task. I had worked hard to banish the memory of that day at the grave, to sweep it from my mind as soon as it arrived. For quite some time, it was a labor I had been free to give up. Now I would have to take the labor on again. The labor of forgetting.

But how could I be angry with her, how could I even imagine there was something that I needed to forgive? She had borne the unbearable, and gone on, taking her place among the living. How could I fail to admire her? I watched her walking down the street, so straight-backed, so resolute, her hair pulled back into a brilliant disciplined knot. Heroic, really. I wanted to run after her and say, "I'll help you. I'll help you to decide. But I'm sure you understand any decision is terrible. Because what happened was so terrible. The most terrible thing in the world.

But I did not go after her. I let her go. I didn't have the heart for it. I am no longer a young man. More and more these days, I find myself quite tired.

LISA GRUENBERG
A Beautiful Day

*In old age, long after his retirement from the engineering
faculty at Syracuse University, my father, Harry Gruenberg,
began to have flashbacks about his life in Vienna before he
escaped in 1939. He also had recurring nightmares about
being buried alive. I realize now the dream was triggered
by his discovery of the details of his parents' murders, details
released by Austria in the late 1990s.*

*"A Beautiful Day" is one of a group of essays and stories
titled* Searching for Mia. *Mia was my father's younger sister,
who disappeared into Germany in 1941 at the age of fifteen.
The essays deal with trying to come to grips with my father's
emerging stories, and my search for his sister, his lost family,
and his friends and neighbors after his death. They also
explore my own experience with depression, and its
relationship to creativity and writing.*

*Josephine Helwing, my father's Aunt Pepi, is one of the
many relatives I try to recreate on the page.*

My father's Aunt Pepi's medical record arrived at our home in 2007, a
full two years after his death. I'd plowed through dozens of documents
in search of my father's lost family, but the brevity of this record documenting the last eight weeks of Pepi's life at Am Steinhof, the mental
institution on the outskirts of Vienna, still shocked me. There are only
ten notes documenting her decline—from her admission note after
she attempted suicide, dated March 7, 1942, to her death certificate
seven weeks later. She was forty-five years old, single, unemployed,
Mosaisch—Jewish. Her final weight was seventy-one pounds. The
cause of death was written in Latin: *Marasmus e Psychosis*—Severe
Malnutrition due to Psychosis. This was not a diagnosis I ever learned
about in medical school.

There was a set of photographs attached to her file. In profile her
head is held up on a post with a label spelling out her last name,

Helwing. Straight on, her mouth is slightly open; her eyes are closed. Her lower lip is swollen, as if she had been struck. I could not tell if the photo was taken when she was dead or alive.

Psychiatrist Viktor Frankl signed Pepi's first evaluation. Frankl survived deportation, concentration camps, and the Death March, and went on to establish a psychiatric institute in Vienna after the war. He wrote a worldwide bestseller, *Man's Search for Meaning: An Introduction to Logotherapy,* describing his particular branch of existential psychiatry honed by his experiences during the Holocaust.

Although Frankl was head of the female suicide ward at Am Steinhof in the 1930s, he was no longer allowed to work there after the *Anschluss,* when Germany annexed Austria in March 1938. He could only recommend admission from the Rothschild Hospital, the Jewish hospital that would be closed down a few months after Pepi's death. Frankl's approach to life reminds me so much of my father's, and of that of so many I interviewed who survived that time and went on to flourish. They carried on by burying part of the past, erasing other memories, and rewriting the remainder of their stories. It's what we all do—a normal response to suffering so that we can live our lives. But in the setting of overwhelming trauma, I wonder if this adjustment of memory is just another kind of madness.

Pepi's admission note stated: "The patient has been psychologically disturbed for the last months…She jumped into the Danube Canal and her mother, who is malnourished and half-blind, can no longer care for her at home." This was my father's maternal grandmother, Sabina Helwing, who would be dispatched on one of the last deportations out of Vienna a few months after her daughter's death at Am Steinhof. Sabina took a passenger train to Theresienstadt in Czechoslovakia on September 10, 1942. She left her luggage on the railway platform and was herded into a cattle car on September 11 and was gassed on arrival in Treblinka.

The note goes on: "For the last two to three days the patient has refused to eat." The note doesn't mention that by 1942, the Jews of Vienna were all starving. Families were forced to share one or two ration cards, and most shops did not allow Jews to enter.

"The patient is dysphoric, agitated, and voices concerns about cleanliness. She is restless and repetitively strokes the bed linens. She admits she hears voices. She is unkempt and incontinent of urine and feces. She says the whole world is against her. She says she knows the assistant physician, 'he lives in my building.' 'The Frau Doctor is my cook.'" Pepi goes on to talk about her husband and children, even though she is childless and unmarried. "'My husband went to America—my mother-in-law is making me *meshuga*.'"

Pepi's pulse was described as "rapid and small." The picture was thought to be consistent with "toxicosis." Frankl states that this is a catatonic picture in the setting of an acute psychosis of menopause. The note finishes with, "The patient was normal before this and there is no family history of mental illness...There is a reactive component to her presentation and there is good hope for recovery." Frankl suggests transfusion with her own blood, and heart medication, as well as tube feeding. There is no evidence that any of those recommendations were followed.

The first time my father mentioned his Aunt Pepi to me was May 2004, when I drove to Syracuse to check in on my parents, right after photographs of prisoner abuses at Abu Ghraib Prison were released. My 83-year-old father was growing frail. Parkinson's slowed his movements and his thinking. It made his already serene visage more wooden, and his speech even quieter and less expressive than usual.

A few days into the visit, we all sat down for breakfast in front of the south-facing windows. I grew up in Syracuse's flat light, so the rare sunshine delighted me. The clouds that clung to the city were a standing joke between my husband, Martin, and our teenaged daughters. Martin took on a thick Viennese accent or my mother's clipped British Columbian speech whenever we hit the wall of precipitation that almost always met us on the Thruway outside Rome, New York.

His version of my father: "*Ach,* it's *shnowing!*" My Canadian mother's voice: "Pull up your socks, it's just another spot of bother!" Martin's imitations made the girls laugh. I didn't find them funny. I couldn't hear my parents' accents.

"Such a gorgeous day," my mother said as she whacked the top off her soft-boiled egg.

My father fiddled with the "Saturday" compartment of his day-of-the-week medicine holder; my mother reached across the table, took the dispenser from him, and handily opened it, dumping the contents into the china bowl next to his orange juice. My father took his pills one by one, rinsing them down with tepid coffee. When his hands settled in his lap, the tremor of Parkinson's took over. He stared out the window as if too exhausted to pick up his spoon.

In the garden, tulips broke through the dirt. My frugal mother's used pantyhose restrained vines against the picket fence. Cotton crotches waited for leaves to cover their immodest display. "What a beautiful day!" My father turned to me suddenly, speaking as if these next words flowed out of my mother's last sentence about the weather. His voice was steady; he didn't clear his throat the way he usually did. "A few days after Hitler marched into Vienna, it was a day just like this one. We needed to leave the flat to look for food, even though the streets were dangerous. My parents asked me to walk to the Second District to check on Grandmother Sabina and my mother's younger sister, Pepi. There was glass everywhere, and on doors and across storefronts was written JEW or DIRTY JEW."

My mother stood up and muttered, "Here we go again." Even though her egg was only half eaten, she grabbed the cardigan from the back of her chair and went out to work in the garden. This wasn't the first time in the past few years that my father suddenly segued into the 1930s when I visited, but it was a calmer transition compared with outbreaks I witnessed before, and he spoke in English rather than breaking into German, the way he had with earlier flashbacks.

"I was seventeen," he continued. "It was a beautiful day just like this one. A crowd gathered around something, and they were laughing and talking." My father's voice was modulated, not the usual quiet monotone.

"Dad?" I always tried to speak to my father when he veered into the past. But this wasn't the father I knew; I sensed it wasn't me he was talking to.

"I walked to the edge of the crowd and then pushed my way to the inside of their circle. They were watching what appeared to be a pile of rags moving in the dirt."

A man lay on the ground. It was an orthodox Jew with a long beard and forelocks, his dark clothes covered with dust, his face bloody from a beating. The man moaned and struggled to stand.

"The Jew begged for help," my father said. "A young woman, dressed in a blue suit, moved into the center of the circle." Wavy hair framed her lovely face. She grinned and winked at the crowd. She smiled down on the man with an expression of pity, and reached down as if to help him up. He lifted his hand to hers. Turning again to the crowd, she circled her hips. She raised her skirt up over the tops of her stockings as she continued to gyrate, and then straddled the man who slumped back to the ground.

My father's eyes weren't old and watery when he told me this; they were the clear eyes of an angry young man. I wanted to touch him across the table, but he seemed very far away. He swallowed twice. "She urinated onto the man's face," he whispered.

My father looked down and then back to me. "What kind of a thing is this for a young boy to see?" He turned back to his soggy Cheerios. He shrunk in front of my eyes; the tremor in his hands returned. A little bit of milk dripped from his lower lip.

"Shall we go for a drive?" he asked.

Once the episodes were over, they were over. I wiped the milk from his face with a paper napkin. He leaned against the table and pushed himself to his feet and waved me away when I got up to help.

"I can manage," he said.

He carried dishes to the sink one at a time. Back and forth he went, using one hand to prop up his thin body on the table, on the counter and back again. He scrubbed each dish with soap and scalding water before placing it in the dishwasher, and steadied himself against the walls to get back to his room to dress.

"I'll get Mom," I called after him.

My mother was digging in the garden.

"Why did you leave?" I asked.

She leaned the shovel against the side of the house and pulled off her gardening gloves. "I don't like to see him upset," she said.

"He was talking about the Anschluss. When was that?"

"Who knows?" She answered as if she were really saying, "who cares?"

"Did he ever talk to you about after the Germans came in?"

"He seems to be talking about the whole thing a lot. Maybe it's that new medication he's on." She deadheaded a few exhausted peonies. "He used to sit across from me for hours and not say a word—forget about actually having a conversation. Then he'd go to his office and close the door. But now you can't get him to stop talking."

"But, Mom, this wasn't just Dad running on with one of his old stories."

"All I know is this stuff comes up at the most inappropriate times with the wrong people." My parents adored each other, but my mother couldn't tolerate the old stories, and she seemed to find my father's outbursts unbearable.

"Who are the right people, Mom?" I pictured my father going off the deep end when I wasn't home. I wondered if my mother continued to fill in *The New York Times* crossword puzzle with ink, maybe patting his hand, waiting for him to come back to himself.

"The past belongs in the past, don't you think?" she said, picking up her shovel again. "You can't change it."

At the end of the day, I asked my father again about the scene he described. He seemed surprised that I knew about it. That was the way it was with the flashbacks. The memory was triggered; the symptoms of Parkinson's disappeared. He often spoke rapidly in German, a language he rarely spoke when we were growing up and certainly never spoke fluently in our presence. Once the flashback emerged, my father regained a chunk of memory, but when he talked about it afterward, it often sounded as if it happened to someone else.

"I saw the white lace of the woman's garter belt," he said. "I thought I saw the shadow of hair between her thighs."

I winced. My father was always so proper. I imagined the urine caught the sunlight and sparkled as it splashed against the Jew's upturned face. The crowd broke into applause. The woman laughed and they roared with her. Some of the men clapped each other on the back. The Jew coughed and then lay still.

"A policeman watched the whole thing and did nothing," my father said. "What would have happened if I walked into that crowd to help the man?" But he turned away and ran up the avenue, toward the Danube Canal and his Grandmother Sabina and Aunt Pepi's house. Passersby moved in slow motion. My father reined himself in to walk with them.

"I had to be careful," he said. "The Nazis changed the traffic rules after the Anschluss, and now the cars were driving on the right side of the street instead of the left." The change threw the city into turmoil. Leaving aside everything that happened in Vienna during the months after the Anschluss—the beatings, the lootings, hundreds of Jews jumping out of windows because they couldn't bear the weight of their lives—just this simple fact of a change in traffic rules, something I hadn't heard about until my father's outburst, added a tactile disruption to the lovely Vienna he constructed for me when I was a child. A world turned mad.

Once in the courtyard of his grandmother Sabina's building, my father took the stairs three at a time. He pounded on the door, but it fell open. He heard Sabina's reedy voice singing a Yiddish lullaby. He told me the gilded mirrors in the salon were all smashed, breaking up reflections of books scattered on the floor. Omama Sabina was one of my father's wealthy relatives. His father was usually unemployed and my father's own family was living hand-to-mouth well before the war.

My father followed the voice into Sabina's bedroom. Pepi sat at her mother's vanity, dressed in a slip, but didn't move to cover herself when my father came in. A bruise in the shape of a hand marred her white neck. "My aunt's dark hair was suddenly streaked with gray," my father told me.

Sabina's silver brush cut furrows in her daughter's hair, and she put a plump finger to her lips when she noticed my father. She led Pepi to bed and pulled down the coverlet. Pepi slipped between the sheets. Sabina moved away but Pepi moaned, then sat up, her eyes wide.

"Don't leave me," she cried. Sabina sat down on the bed.

"Would you make us some tea, Harry?" Sabina asked my father, not taking her eyes off Pepi.

"Where's the maid, Omama?"

"She hasn't come since the Germans arrived."

Christians were no longer allowed to work for Jews after the Anschluss. My father pumped water into a pot, lit the stove, and put the water on. Scraping a circle of mold off a rind of bread, he sliced it and spread it with marmalade. When the tea was ready, he loaded everything on a tray and carried it in. The grandfather clock in the hallway measured empty seconds.

Sabina poured tea into a cup and added a large spoonful of sugar and handed it to Pepi. Pepi held the translucent china in her hands but did not bring it to her lips. My father passed onto the balcony. It grew dim by the canal, and he could barely see the buildings of the Inner City across it.

"An old Jew with a cane hobbled below, and a group of laughing boys chased him," my father said.

"Take off your disguise, old man! Take it off or we will have to help you!"

The old man's breath was heavy and uneven. One of the youths grabbed his shoulder and spun him. Another took hold of his beard and shouted as he yanked on it, "Take off the disguise, old man!" He swung the Jew around by the beard. The cane flew against the side of the building and clattered to the feet of one of the bigger boys. He picked it up and swung it around to the back of the man's head. The sound as it hit the Jew's skull was oddly muffled. The old man dropped to the ground. The boys looked up at the houses that lined the street.

"I jumped back against the balcony doorway," my father said.

At midnight the streets were quiet again, and my father got ready to leave. Sabina threw her arms around his neck. "Harry, don't leave us!"

My father pried her fingers apart. "I'll come back tomorrow, Omama."

Outside, the body of the old Jew was gone. My father walked toward home along the dark canal.

"I thought I heard the boys coming up behind me. I broke into a run." When my father turned off the Ringstraße, he was sure he saw the boys walking toward him on the other side of the street.

"A young woman walked tall and straight in front of me," said my father. "I came up beside her and pretended I was with her. We passed the boys. I think she smiled at me—I think she took my hand."

My father ducked into an alley and made his way home.

When I got ready for bed that evening, I pulled down the family genealogy my father put together after he retired from the Engineering Department at Syracuse University. I barely looked through the weighty binder when he gave me my copy in 1994. There were several pages about history, and then he'd written something about almost everyone, even relatives who died long before the war. His writing was cheerful and full of exclamation points. It didn't match his carefully rendered family trees, so many branches withered with phrases like "perished at Auschwitz" and "died, Minsk?"

I realized he'd written several pages about his great-grandparents but less than half a page on each of his parents, who were deported a few weeks after Pepi died. The story of his younger brother Uri, who was sent on a Kindertransport to Palestine in October 1938, received a few paragraphs. Their youngest sister, Mia, who disappeared into Germany in 1941 when she was just fifteen, did not even have a section of her own.

He wrote that Pepi stayed on with her mother when her five siblings married. In the '60s, his brother Uri located her pauper's grave in the Jewish section of the Zentralfriedhof, the central cemetery of Vienna. My father doesn't mention visiting the grave himself, even though he and my mother visited Austria many times as tourists. Those visits now seem incongruous to me.

I asked my father about Pepi again the next morning. He remembered her as shy and withdrawn. "She was a little pathetic," he said, but he couldn't come up with any details. "She and Sabina were badly beaten on Kristallnacht. I wonder if she might have been raped. She could have been subject of medical experiments, or she might have been euthanized." He said all those things in his expressionless Parkinson's voice.

After the visit, I decided I needed to get down the "real story" once and for all. My father agreed to allow me to videotape him a few weeks later. It would turn out to be his last visit to our home in Boston.

At the beginning of the first videotape a stuffed chair fills the screen. My father talks to me off camera and then shuffles into view. His back is bent so that he has to angle his head up to look forward. Watching the tapes now, I can't help but think of my father-in-law, Marty, who was in a nursing home at that time, biding his time while cancer finished digesting his bones. His vertebrae collapsed into that same pitiful C.

I begin. "When all these things came up, Dad, I thought, 'Well, it's not so important now. You lived a long life without telling these stories.'"

"Well, I think you know I was writing about this, but then—I don't know—in order to write about it correctly you have to organize it and think about it."

He tells me, as he does often throughout the tapes, "It's the history that I really want to get down on paper." He stares at the camera and meanders through history or drones about his happy life before the Anschluss. Sometimes there is the clank of dishes in the background, or a hushed conversation between my mother and me captured on tape. My father's quiet voice marches on. His eyes seem to search for something beyond the lens.

He unfolds the old narratives in the same way he did for me as a child, even though I can recite all the punch lines with him. He skips the events of Kristallnacht in November 1938, the subject of one of his first flashbacks. He jumps to a tired version of crossing the border into

Belgium in March 1939. "A soldier told me we couldn't keep any currency," he said, "so I flushed my few pfennigs down the WC." He speaks as if he is telling me someone else's story. In this third person version, he and the other Jewish boys and young men traveling with him threw their caps in the air when they crossed the border into Belgium. He leaves out the parts I heard during other flashbacks, about his rail car being uncoupled and pulled off track; he omits the dog straining on the soldier's leash, his description of the soldier's eyes, one blue and one green. The soldier forced him and the other Jewish teenagers to play Russian roulette until the next train came along and they were reconnected and sent on their merry way.

Listening to the tapes now I feel the same impatience I felt when I sat with my father. I keep on thinking, "the history has been written, I want to know what *you* saw and experienced."

He describes in detail his work at the Zionist training farm in the south of England and repeats a lighthearted version of his arrest by the British fourteen months later, in June 1940. He was incarcerated at a ramshackle seaside hotel on the Isle of Man with hundreds of other Jews. Ostensibly, the British were afraid of spies. Every other day soldiers escorted a group through the barbed wire surrounding the hotel, and my father swam in the frigid waters of the Irish Sea under armed guard. Local girls flirted with the soldiers while my father toweled himself off with a monogrammed towel.

He was shipped out at the end of that summer and imprisoned in POW camps in Quebec and New Brunswick for the next year and a half. Other Jews who were interned by the British were bitter about those lost years. My father focused on the education he received from the Jewish professors and the rabbi incarcerated with him. He spoke about that time as if it were a brief hiatus in his otherwise uneventful life.

The rabbi and my father were released in December 1941, right after Pearl Harbor. My father's Uncle Menio, one of Pepi's four brothers, had managed to escape Vienna via the free port of Shanghai and then was sponsored by the Jewish Community in Salt Lake City. But my father wasn't allowed to cross the border to join him, because he was considered to be an "enemy alien." Menio found my father a sponsor in Vancouver, so he went there, finding himself a job as a janitor. He talked his way into the third year of the University of British Columbia in 1943, and graduated at the top of his class in 1946.

His roommate, Mel, who was engaged to my mother's sister Phyllis, brought my father home for his first Christmas dinner in 1943. By then, my father had lost contact with his family, but had no idea that almost everyone he left behind had already been slaughtered. In a photograph from my mother's album, labeled "our first meeting with Harry," my father sits uncomfortably on the sofa next to his future wife, her sister, and Mel. A Christmas tree looms behind him.

"The rest is history!" was the way my father always put it.

I took my first trip to Vienna in 2006, a full year after my father's death. I went to trace his family and neighbors, but also to visit his old haunts. I walked along the canal to Pepi and Sabina's home on Obere Donaustraße, with the Danube Canal on one side and whizzing traffic on the other. Cracks fissured the façade at number 65, perhaps left by mortar fire when the Second District became the battleground between German and Russian troops toward the end of the war. The balcony where my father witnessed an old man's murder still extended off the second floor.

I was still trying to hang my father's old stories and outbursts onto the framework of history. The Anschluss was in March 1938. My father was thrown out of school that June. Kristallnacht followed in November, and my father would leave Vienna for England alone, in March 1939, at the age of eighteen.

In a letter written to Uri in Palestine, my father's cousin, 15-year-old Kurt Helwing, Pepi's nephew, recounts the events of Kristallnacht. My father's most vivid flashback was about the events described in this letter. This is one of the few family letters that openly talks about the events of that night. Kurt was already in England, having been sent on a children's transport soon after Kristallnacht, so he didn't have to worry about censors.

> Dear Uri!
> I want to tell you a few things about Vienna after November 10. They took away the keys to our apartment. We did not get the keys to our apartment back for another 14 days, but then we were forced to give up the flat by 10 December. [Jews were systematically moved out of their homes and forced to move in with other families, mostly in the Second District.] So we moved in with Omama. There, all mirrors, some of the

windows, the radio, a table and two chairs had been smashed. Your parents were also driven from their home and their keys were taken away from them. In the evening, Göring announced on the radio that all had blown over, so your parents went back home with a second set of keys and went to bed. In the morning the Nazis came back and took away the second set of keys. After about a week they got the keys back [my father's mother had to go to Gestapo headquarters to get the keys]. Your flat was ransacked. The suitcase from Germany [with supplies for Uri], the lamp, which Harry had made at school, and 1.50 German Marks that Mia had saved, were all gone. Uncle Sisko [one of Pepi's brothers], Uncle Simel [Sabina's brother-in-law], and Ludwig [Simel's son] were all arrested. Uncle Simel was released soon after, but Sisko and Ludwig were sent to Dachau. Ludwig is still there.

My father translated this letter and a number of family letters from 1938 and early 1939. He promised to translate the rest for me, but he never did. Many of the letters were illegible; they were often written in code to avoid the censors. Even after he died, when I hired a translator, it was hard to understand what was going on in these one-sided conversations, and many of the later letters, from 1941 to 1942, were missing from my father's files.

I have no doubt that the events my father described during and after his flashbacks happened, but if they happened exactly as he remembered them, I have to doubt. The broken mirrors in Kurt's letter would suggest my father's memory of the events of the Anschluss actually happened months later, on Kristallnacht. My father's concern that she might have been raped was impossible to substantiate. Many Austrians and Germans who researched the Holocaust said it would have been unusual for a Jewish woman to be raped by a gentile during this period, but I wonder.

Pepi wrote to my father in England right after he fled, two years before her hospitalization at Am Steinhof. When she wrote this letter, she and Sabina hadn't been forced out of their home yet to an apartment they shared with distant cousins, a few blocks in from the canal. The letter belies my father's description of Pepi as addled and incapable.

Vienna 3. April. 1939
Dear Harry!

I have a big favor to ask of you—if you would be so nice as to follow the advice of Mrs. Novak, who lives in our building, by going to her son and his cousin, Alfred Eiberschütz, so that, with his reference, I will be able to obtain a house maid or nanny position in England. Mrs. Novak's son is a British citizen and, according to his mother, a nice young man. He is 24 years old and married to a British woman.

Mr. Alfred Eiberschütz is a member of B'nai B'rith and would be very obliging if you needed anything. Mrs. Novak asks you to give greetings to her cousin and her son and daughter-in-law from her mother, Ms. Dr. Clara Kraus, and from her as well.

Dear Harry. I hope you are in good health and write to me soon.

Greetings
Your Aunt Pepi

Those still trapped in Vienna had to visit numerous bureaucratic offices to get permissions to leave Austria, but then they also had to find a place that would offer them an entry visa, and those visas were becoming harder and harder to come by. Many sought positions in Britain as domestic servants. Thousands would be deported and murdered because countries like the United States and Britain did not allow them entry. Aunt Pepi was only one of many relatives writing my eighteen-year-old father to find them a place. He didn't have a clue how to help any of them, and then Britain declared war and he was arrested and deported.

One of the archivists I befriended in Vienna suggested I go in person to Am Steinhof: to locate Pepi's medical record, to see an exhibit on Nazi euthanasia, and to visit the Otto Wagner church built on the grounds. I took a cab from Pepi's home and was dropped off inside the entrance of an enormous compound. A patient interrupted a conversation with himself to ask me for a cigarette. I hadn't realized that Freud and Viktor Frankl's institution was still in use as a mental hospital. I headed uphill toward the dome of the church, passed locked wards and a cemetery, then tried to catch my breath as I walked into the vast gallery of the exhibit hall.

Dozens of children stared at me from photographs. Some had cleft lips, others the features of Down syndrome. Many looked perfectly normal. The captions told me that several hundred children had been murdered at Am Steinhof as part of the Nazi euthanasia program, designed to purify the Master Race.

At the end of the hall was an office, and sitting at the desk was a red-haired boy I recognized from one of the many archives in town. Young Austrians can avoid military service by working on projects focused on the Holocaust. He turned to his books when I came to the door, but his burning cheeks gave away that he recognized me from an earlier visit at the Archives of the Austrian Resistance.

"Can you tell me how to find the central office?" I asked.

"I have no idea," he answered without looking up.

"Perhaps you could look up the phone number?"

"There is no way to get this information."

"But surely you could tell me where the administrative offices are?"

The boy looked up at me finally, with an expression that clearly communicated he thought my request was inappropriate or even perverted, a look I had gotten used to in Vienna and Germany. I wonder if this attitude kept my father from pushing for more information about his family. He grew up in a world where getting on the wrong side of a bureaucrat could get you killed; I did not. By the time I wandered the grounds and found the main office, the doors were locked; Wednesdays they closed early. A young woman was getting into her car and I ran down the steps to her. "I came a long way, and I am trying to locate a medical record from wartime."

The woman smiled as if this happened every day. She handed me her business card and waited for mine; on this first trip, I hadn't known that everyone in Austria had cards. "I will contact the director, Dr. Eberhard Gabriel. He will be more than happy to locate those records for you." She hesitated, as if still waiting for my card. "Call me tomorrow," she said.

There was nothing left to be done. I went back up the hill, following the signs to the church. The guidebook said that they allowed Otto Wagner to build here because he was too radical for the time. What better place for the building of a madman than the outskirts of the city, on the grounds of a mental hospital? I walked into the soaring white nave, sparsely trimmed in gold leaf. I sat in one of the pews. It was hard to feel meditative when I thought about the murdered children buried in tidy rows outside. I tried to focus on the ceiling.

I realized that I began mourning my father before he died—not the old man I captured on the video screen, but the young man I never knew, who smiles shyly from old photographs. I always sensed a void at the center of my father's love, and I think I traveled to Vienna to find the source of that feeling. Maybe his love for me was really a love for something left behind—richer for that reason, but, also, less real.

An older couple approached me when I exited the back of the church. Big hands and feet hung from the man's narrow limbs. I refit my father's small smile into the man's round face. He held the elbow of a woman with mirthful eyes. They struck up a conversation with me.

"Don't you love Vienna?" the woman asked. Everyone in Vienna asked me this.

"*Yah, yah.*" I couldn't explain to her my horror that life went on here as if nothing ever happened, or my guilt about not coming when my father was still alive. Vienna heightened all my sensations; her beauty lacerated me. I couldn't see the city without putting her through the prism of my father's flashbacks.

But even after he recovered some of his memory, my father still thought of Vienna as the most delightful place. The first and only chapter of his unfinished memoirs, written after the flashbacks started, begins with a popular song from that time:

'Vienna, Vienna, only you will always be the city of my dreams!'...
In spite of the hardships my family experienced and the times when there was not enough money for food, I feel I had a very happy childhood. And I was in love with Vienna!

Without the Holocaust, my father might have married the woman with mirthful eyes and continued to live here. My brothers and I would not exist. The couple said goodbye and supported each other as they walked up the steps and into the church.

I walked out of the compound into a wide park with a gentle view to the Vienna Woods. Couples and families walked hand in hand, enjoying the sun slanting on lush fields and lighting up Vienna in the distance. Here I thought my father invented the late-afternoon stroll; our neighbors in Syracuse eyed us as if the activity were somewhat suspicious. But those walks were yet another preserved island from my father's former life. The memory gave me the odd feeling I had arrived home.

On my last visit to Vienna in 2007, I finally met with Dr. Eberhard Gabriel at an outdoor café in the Inner City. He had retired as the director of Am Steinhof and had just published his book about the history of the institution. Eberhard looked me straight in the eyes and shook my hand warmly with both of his.

"It's wonderful to meet you finally," he said. I liked him immediately.

Over coffee and strudel, we went over Pepi's record together. He told me that although she should have been on a separate ward for Jews, they didn't have the staffing to segregate her. He confirmed there was nothing in the record to support that she was euthanized, or that she was a subject of medical experiments. Family never visited before she died; the trams were closed to Jews and it would have been too far to walk. I wondered if there was information missing from the record, and why there was such a long delay between her death and her burial by the Jewish community. But I couldn't bring myself to ask Eberhard when we met; I don't remember what inhibited me. Maybe I thought it was impolite after he'd gone to so much trouble to have the record sent to me.

Eberhard acknowledged that the Nazi years were a sad chapter in the history of Am Steinhof, but he was clearly proud of the advancements made in the care of patients with mental illness in the years preceding and following the war.

"There is no way to know for sure what happened," Eberhard said as he flipped through Pepi's chart. "She arrived starving. She had an ear infection at one point. She probably just died of neglect."

"And the photographs? Was she dead or alive?"

"Alive, definitely. That would have been quite routine."

"But her head is on a post," I pointed at the photograph.

Eberhard moved his pastry to one side and considered the pictures. "She was catatonic," he said. "Quite routine." he said again.

I'd learned that Frankl and his wife obtained visas to the United States in 1941, but he didn't want to leave his parents, so he let the visas lapse. His father died at Theresienstadt, his mother was murdered in Auschwitz, his wife in Bergen-Belsen. In his book, *Man's Search for Meaning,* Frankl wrote about a vision he had during the waning days of the war. He'd been separated from his wife and had no idea where she was. He and other prisoners were being driven along by cruel guards.

Hiding his mouth behind his upturned collar, the man marching next to me whispered suddenly: "If our wives could see us now! I do hope they are better off in their camps and don't know what is happening to us."

That brought thoughts of my own wife to mind. And as we stumbled on for miles, slipping on icy spots, supporting each other time and again, dragging one another up and onward, nothing was said, but we both knew: each of us was thinking of his wife.

Occasionally I looked at the sky, where the stars were fading and the pink light of the morning was beginning to spread behind a dark bank of clouds. But my mind clung to my wife's image, imagining it with an uncanny acuteness. I heard her answering me, saw her smile, her frank and encouraging look. Real or not, her look was then more luminous than the sun which was beginning to rise.

A thought transfixed me: for the first time in my life I saw the truth as it is set into song by so many poets, proclaimed as the final wisdom by so many thinkers. The truth—that love is the ultimate and the highest goal to which man can aspire. Then I grasped the meaning of the greatest secret that human poetry and human thought and belief have to impart: The salvation of man is through love and in love.

Viktor Frankl knew his wife and his parents were gone when he wrote these words in 1946. Did he really think of his wife as he stumbled along? Is that really how he survived, or is that how he chose to remember?

Eberhard cleared his throat.

"Do you think survivors rewrite memories to find meaning?" I asked him.

"I think we all do."

"And is it common for survivors to have flashbacks when they get older?"

"Oddly, it's when they get older that it often starts. I don't know if it's time that wears them down, makes it harder to compartmentalize memory, or if it's illness, or medications, like the ones your father took."

"When he told me these stories, I didn't know what to do."

"Maybe you didn't need to do anything. He chose to tell you these things. Maybe you just needed to listen."

We sat together for some time in silence, watching tourists strolling by the Stephansdom.

"Isn't Vienna lovely in spring?" Eberhard asked me.

"Yes," I said, stirring my second coffee mélange, releasing its pungent scent. When I spoke again, I had trouble keeping my voice from shaking. "My father used to cringe when I hugged him, like my touch burned him." I took a sip of coffee. "And he never said I love you unless I said it first. People tell me that's generational, but he never once told my brothers he loved them. He never hugged them."

"The reason for that is obvious, don't you think?" Eberhard looked at me as if he weighed his decision to elucidate or not. "He loved his family. In the end, he lost them. Maybe it felt too dangerous to say it out loud."

He signaled for the bill. "When will you visit us again?"

"I feel like I'm finished here," I said. "I don't think I will ever return."

My father lived another year after I finished videotaping him. His nightmares vanished and he never had another outburst. Perhaps, as Frankl and my friend Eberhard suggest, we tell stories to make meaning of our lives. I write mine down in order to find strength to move on. Putting this on paper, I feel my own skin growing less porous. But my father and his family remain inside me. Their memories continue, clear in my mind.

It was never emptiness I sensed at the center of my father's love. At his core lay a void that drew in yearning—yearning for connection and for the people he lost. My search for our missing pieces left me aware of the joyous depths of my own life. As unsentimental as I've always been, I feel that joy when I catch up with my 93-year-old mother, still sharp as ever. I see it when I gaze at our daughters, both healthy and strong. I sense its warm weight when Martin's arm settles over my shoulder. Even folding laundry sometimes feels like a prayer.

I think back to my last conversation with my father in 2005. My father-in-law finally succumbed the day before. The beds upstairs were unmade, dishes were piled in the sink, and the floors were sticky with bits of food and dirt tracked in by family passing through. I sat at my desk with a mug of strong coffee, almost dozing in warmth, feeling the pleasure of a sunny afternoon without the need to comfort anyone.

When I picked up the receiver, I knew it was my father.

"Hi, Dad," I said into the silence.

We spoke for close to an hour that day. I pulled out my questions about his family and neighbors. I scrawled his answers into the margins of my notebook with purple ink. Those were the last questions I asked him about the past. I didn't want to tire him out, and I figured we could finish up another time.

"No imposition," he said. "None of this bothers me anymore."

A few days before that call, my father had been in a head-on collision. He and the other driver walked away from the accident, but their cars were totaled. My father's neck bothered him, so he drove himself to the emergency room in my mother's car. The doctors overlooked the small vein seeping blood into his brain. The morning after this conversation, he would wake with a blinding headache. My mother sent him off for a nap. He never woke up again.

"How are you feeling since the accident?" I asked him.

"I don't think I'll drive anymore."

I wrote that down—"No more driving!" underlining it three times.

Out of the blue, my father asked. "Well, how are you doing with all this with Marty?" My father-in-law was a difficult man, but I'd come to love him in the long months leading up to his death. I started to cry.

Thinking back on that last conversation now, I can see my young father standing in front of me, and for the first time, I hear his thick accent saying his last words to me. "Don't worry about asking about the past. You know, despite everything, I had a wonderful childhood. I was loved—when you come down to it, that's the only thing that really matters."

And I remember now, what came next.

"I love you, Lisa."

"I love you too, Dad."

Then we both hung up.

KATHLEEN HALME
Note

Somewhere there is order,
a multiverse of order.
I could have
sewed that rip in the lining
with special strong thread,
washed pillows for the refugees,
cut new gardenias to replace
the yellowed blouses collapsed
in the vase, called someone,
hoping they'd be happy
to hear from me. I

could have faced the hard time
with the fortitude of my tribe,
planted elephant garlic,
loved you through this world,
yet I took time
to assign my pocket watch, best locket,
and gems to friends and sisters,
spread the satin wedding dress
out on the big table
for the inevitable.

Now the pills are marvelous. I
feel the tremendousness of love.

JENNIFER HANNO
The Case for Psychic Distance

Tell us a little about yourself. Just so we can get to know each other. What you do for a living, what you love to read, a little about you as a writer and, of course, what you want to get out of this course. Include a picture if you'd like. It's very helpful.

This shouldn't be hard, you think. After all, you don't even need to leave your house. You sit down in front of the computer to review your life. As you wait for inspiration, your eyes drift to the window; a single red bug heralds what upstate New York calls spring. It dawns on you that you haven't done much in the last four months—2.5 loads of laundry a week seem hardly worth mentioning.

You wonder how much you should write. Too much will seem pretentious and too little will be off-putting. You do a draft for each. Then one more for good measure. You throw in a load of whites and decide to wait to see what the others will post. Besides, you don't want to appear overeager by being the first.

After you organize the spice cupboard, you check the class page and find all seventeen members of the class have submitted their assignments. Now you'll be the last, leaving the instructor with the impression that you are possibly a slacker and definitely not one to embrace risk. You get to work perusing your classmates' bios so you can decide which of yours to use. Virginia has degrees in chemical engineering and physics and lives and works in Barcelona with her partner. She has written two novels "just for fun" and now feels she would like to "test her edges" with short fiction. Julianna lives in California where she is working on a new film. Her last documentary won an award you never heard of but which sounds impressive. She enjoys mountain climbing and Russian literature. She, too, has two degrees, both from Columbia, and is a former Miss Vermont.

The list goes on and your heart sinks deeper into your chest. Your classmates have careers and goals and publishing credits. They hail from California, London, Syria, and Hong Kong. The guy on the phone assured you this class was for beginners. Bastard.

Best to go with the short version of your bio, you conclude. No need to mention why you are no longer teaching. Might also be best to leave out your history at Jefferson Community College and definitely your part-time job at McDonald's.

You also decide to change out of your pajamas.

Remember to call the Adult Literacy Center and cancel. Last week Pedro stared at your breasts the entire time you were trying to prep him for the citizenship test. Besides, you need to concentrate on your writing. Ignore the flashing light on the answering machine and get to work.

Instead of a picture of yourself, you upload a picture of your tallest cactus.

Apparently, "to develop our own craft, we must study the craft of others who have mastered the art." Thus, there are weekly reading assignments on which you are to comment. You read the first short story carefully, making notes in the margins. It's abstract, but you think you've got it. You check out the discussion question you are supposed to answer: *How does the story fulfill the contract the writer makes with the reader?*

You return to the text. As far as you can tell, it's about a man who decides to hunt a bear. There is no mention of a contract for either man or bear.

You write copious notes of possible responses to the question you don't understand, then wait to see what others say.

Others say most of what was in your notes. You got nothing now.

Writing Assignment No. 1: The first paragraph is crucial to your narrative. Write the opening of a short story with the first line, "It happened on the stairs." Begin in the middle of things. Hook the reader immediately. The reader should know what the character wants. We are what we want. Character is destiny. That's what makes the reader care. We must know who the narrator is. What is his relationship to the other characters, what does he look like, feel, want in life?

In 300 words.

You take a story you have written. Your friend Amy loved it and it could have started in a stairwell. You realize quickly that 300 words is not very many and so you carve away, gutting the phrases Amy loved. What you have left is a sad skeleton, but hey, this is only Assignment 1. You do want to leave room to grow.

No more waiting for others. She who hesitates leaves herself open to suggestions of plagiarism, or worse. You post first thing Thursday morning, your name now at the top of the list. Virginia's the next to post. You read it, your grin growing wider with every sentence.

You suppress a giggle of what could only be described as nefarious glee. You knew it! You knew she couldn't be good at everything! You choose your words carefully when you write your response to her assignment. A new writer doesn't need criticism as much as she needs encouragement. You can be positive; you can find something. Shake your head in pity for your physics-laden classmate. Move the answering machine to the far edge of the desk to make room for your sandwich. Then sit back and wait to see how the professor will deal with this one.

Turns out he loves it. Says it's brilliant; it has a lyrical quality; he can't wait to read more of her magical prose.

You reread the instructor's profile and recheck his credits.

His response to your submission is a little less enthusiastic. He says he wants to experience the scenes more clearly, through vivid detail, and to know the relationship of the narrator to the event more clearly. Grimly, you realize that is all the stuff you cut out when trying to get it down to 300 words. In the interest of self improvement, you reread your piece. *A naive English teacher walks into the weight room to find her principal having sex with the phys ed teacher on a yoga mat. She adroitly records the incident on her iPhone and posts it on Facebook.* After some consideration, you disregard his suggestion to make the scene more vivid. You are not a writer of porn, for God's sake. You look to your peers for some backup here, but they follow the leader, echoing his words. "Thank you for sharing," they all say. The refrain has a dull thud of finality to it.

At this point, you're having serious second thoughts about this instructor, despite his alleged credentials. In fact, the picture he posted of himself in that Yankees baseball cap looks a bit shady, now that you think about it. Print it off and post it on the corkboard over your computer. Perhaps his staring down on you with those condescending eyes will inspire you to find your voice.

At the end of week one, he posts an enthusiastic e-mail in which he praises your class for your "insightful" and "thoughtful" responses to his questions and to each other's work. He is "so excited" at the level of some people's writing! Some of you have really impressed him! You realize you are not part of the impressive club and feel the same way you felt in third grade when Kate Conondario formed a club of girls who had the same sneakers, the ones your mother refused to buy you. You keenly remember the pain of exclusion.

Draw a Nazi mustache on your instructor's picture, and get to work on Assignment 2. You must write a scene in which two characters get into an argument. Both characters desire something, but their desires must be subtly revealed through subtext. Show, don't tell.

At this point, painful memories of Show and Tell threaten to cloud your writing. Block these out. Do not become caught up in the memory of a turtle named Franklin that you brought to Kindergarten in a shoe box. Forget about Franklin's tragic death when Kate Conondario persuaded you to put him in the cage with her pet ferret so they could be friends.

Instead, write a story about a once popular girl whose life takes a turn for the worse when she gets knocked up at seventeen. The stress of the unwanted pregnancy, early marriage to a tattoo artist, and subsequent poverty cause her to develop alopecia areata and lose all her hair. At the age of thirty, broke, overweight, and bald, she seeks employment at her former high school, where she's hired as a Lunch Lady. Name her Kate Conondario.

Taking the position that a hairnet is not only unnecessary in her case but also a violation of her civil liberties, she refuses to wear one while serving. This leads to a full blown argument with the principal, who has stopped in the cafeteria for a pork steak sandwich. But stay focused. Remember the guidelines of the assignment—thinly veiled motivation. What do the characters want? What motivates them? Insert some subtle suggestions that the principal secretly desires the overlarge chocolate chip cookie but his lover, the phys ed teacher, has told him he is developing Middle-Aged Spread. Meanwhile, Kate Conondario's sharp eye recognizes male-pattern baldness in the principal despite his toupee, which, as it turns out, she secretly desires.

Hit send.

Your homework done, take a few moments to change the cat litter. The soft pinging sound of incoming e-mails is drowned out when you sit down to catch up on the latest episode of that show Amy told you about. Vocal cords pit themselves against one another while a glamorous triumvirate renders judgment. Who will go on to the next round?

Of course, this may bring to mind Natalie who sang so beautifully at the fall concert.

Change the channel if this happens.

By the time you check your class page again, the Discussion Board has exploded into a flood of comments, most of which concern the work of Caroline Cho, an American living in Hong Kong. She has based her story on her family's past; apparently, her mother's mother was sold into some sort of geisha arrangement at a young age and shipped to America. After years in the sex trade, she escaped. Perhaps because of this, Caroline has never felt as though she belongs in America. But how can she feel at home in the land that enslaved her ancestors?

Seriously, some people get all the luck. Take a moment to curse your family tree, Caucasian and white bread; accept that you will not be able to count on your family for any good material. Your parents couldn't even offer you a messy divorce.

Seethe as your instructor heaps praise on Caroline Cho's brave choice to write of her family's dark past. By now, you have the sinking sense that your story of public high school intrigue will be overshadowed by Cho's tale of culture lost and found, and you are correct. The instructor feels Kate Conondario needs some "fleshing out." We are not close enough to her. We need to know more about her. He suggests you play the "What if?" game with this character. Throw her into a series of hypothetical situations and see what she does!

Even now, it's all about Kate Conondario, isn't it?

However, the suggestion has merit. Amuse yourself with this game for a while.

What if Kate Conondario trips over the wrestling mats left in the hallway and is knocked unconscious?

What if her body is overlooked by the wrestlers—they've been smoking pot in the locker room—and is rolled up in the mats and stored away for the long weekend?

What if Kate Conondario extricates herself from the wrestling mat, dazed and confused, only to find herself caught in fate's path once again when the pep rally goes horribly wrong. A throng of adolescents rushes out of the gym in moblike fervor, trampling her beneath their Sperrys?

Be encouraged by all the new possibilities you have uncovered!

But, the *What If?* game only works in fiction. Elsewhere, use it with caution.

The answering machine whirs and clicks, but there's no time for that. Week three is upon you and your instructor is *very excited* to see what you will do with this week's concept, something you've never heard of until now: Psychic Distance.

Now we're talking! Your aunt is a psychic, crazy Aunt Veronica! Just last week, she hooked you up with Uncle Harold, who died years ago in a power-line mishap.

But alas, no. It turns out psychic distance is the "degree of emotional detachment maintained toward a person or event." Sadly, it has nothing to do with mediums and out of body encounters, which is disappointing to say the least. The instructor suggests that everyone create a character and experiment with varying levels of psychic distance.

You sit down to begin, but you can't possibly concentrate with your desk lamp flickering. How can you work under these conditions? Venture out to Walmart in search of a new lamp. Fine, stop at the cemetery again, but don't stay long.

Back at your brightly lit desk, search your past for someone to write about. Decide on Franklin. Write a story about a tender-hearted kindergartener who takes her beloved turtle to school one day only to witness his violent death by ferret. You opt for the greatest emotional distance, describing with calm detachment the way the she-devil latched onto Franklin's delicate throat.

Hit send.

Then clean your house, top to bottom. In fact, don't stop there, but clean out the medicine cupboard, arranging your sleeping pills in alphabetical order. Delete all the extraneous items on your desktop, delete all the junk from your e-mail, delete the messages on your answering machine, including the ones from your school. Simplify! Simplify!

Feel good about what you have accomplished. Your life in order, you can now sit down to check out the response to Franklin's demise, but you are distracted by the number of comments about the piece submitted by a student named Baseema, who grew up in Homs. Try to remain calm as you read her story.

It's about a helpless turtle that is fed to a ferret. Oh, and the class is excited about the extended metaphor at work in this tale. The ferret is the oppressive Syrian government and the turtle, the innocent commoners of Syria, whose turtle shell is not strong enough to save them from tyranny, represented by the ferret. The young child who unwittingly brings the turtle to its brutal death is wearing an Uncle Sam T-shirt so the symbolically impaired among us will understand that he represents America.

At this point, it is perfectly permissible to release a string of expletives to your cat. She blinks sympathetically and you open a can of tuna for her. Then you construct a terse but carefully worded e-mail to the asshole who is your teacher.

Express, as professionally and tastefully as you can, your concerns about academic dishonesty. Call his attention to the time at which your piece was submitted and the time thieving Baseema sent hers. Call attention to the striking parallels between them. They are both about turtles killed by ferrets, for God's sake. Make your best appeal for justice in an unjust world.

Steel yourself for the response that follows. Sure, there are a few similarities between the two stories, he says, but they are completely different representations of the turtle metaphor.

Do not reply. Do not, under any circumstances, reveal that you were not writing metaphorically. Instead, take a break from writing and let your creativity find another outlet. Possibly Photoshop. Discover that you can take your professor's face and scan it onto a variety of different body types: Newt Gingrich, Angelina Jolie, Napoleon Bonaparte. No need to choose your favorite; make a collage. Then export it to Walmart and have it put on a coffee cup and a mouse pad.

Week four arrives without a flourish. It is devoted to "the point of narration." Your instructor explains this is *when* the story is narrated in relation to the events described. He asks you to consider the linear plot of "A Good Man Is Hard to Find" and compare it to the modular plot of "A Rose for Emily." Note the way both authors build suspense. As writers, we have the power to manipulate time, the power to create distance from events, giving the narrator the freedom to comment on them. You think this over. It's an appealing idea, but you've hit a wall.

Maybe it's the incessant calls and e-mails from your principal who assures you that you still have a job when you are ready to return. You wonder if that is fear you hear in his voice? Maybe it's the call from the president of the teachers' union, who leaves a message about some Employee Assistance program. Maybe it's your mother's constant advice to "get back on the horse" and call the school. Maybe it's Amy, who won't stop nagging you to call this new doctor...

Or maybe it's because you need a hat!

After all, your instructor is wearing a New York Yankees hat in his picture. Perhaps all writers wear hats. Find your Red Sox hat and put it on. Stare your professor down and revel in the fact that the Sox are doing well this season and the Yankees are out.

Forget Kate Conondario. You need a new character. Make yourself a man.

Name him Alfred. It's a nice name and he's a nice guy. He works at the hardware store. No! The drug store. He's a pharmacist who fills prescriptions all day: Zoloft, Lexapro, Prozac, Cymbalta…

He's not married but lives with his…cat. You rummage around in Alfred's head for a while and learn that he likes euchre and polka dancing. This is probably why he is not married. Of course, Alfred needs a problem, some defining event from which you can find a point of narration. He could get into trouble at work? He's privy to all kinds of secrets. Did he violate privacy laws? Betray a confidence? Or perhaps he saw something? Confronted someone?

This is where you hit a wall again because you know Alfred. He hates confrontation. He is neither hero nor villain. Alfred is loyal. Alfred is responsible, Alfred is…

Boring.

Do not disturb the universe, you tell him as you erase him. You watch with satisfaction as the cursor swallows him up one letter at a time. He goes quietly, without a whimper.

At first, you are relieved he's gone, but what is left in front of you is a blank screen. The blankness of it is hard to take. It's worse than Alfred.

You begin again and again, but that white screen swallows up whatever you say. The right words are beyond your grasp. You can no longer ignore that voice whispering back at you, whispering the uncontestable accusation that you are nothing but a coward.

And a failure.

You cannot find the right distance between you and your failure, can you?

Go ahead and quit. You have things to catch up on anyway. With all this writing nonsense, you are behind on a whole season of *Breaking Bad*. Spend the next eight to twelve hours on this. While you're at it, throw in a season of *Downton Abbey*. One series blends seamlessly into the next as the hours slip away.

Several days later, when a succession of season finales cuts off your escape route one channel at a time, face that screen again. You have an e-mail from your professor. Like all the other e-mails, it stares at you until you open it.

Where have you been? I hope my comments on your writing were not discouraging; they were not meant to be. But I wonder if, perhaps, Kate Conondario and Franklin are hiding the story you really want to tell? Sometimes stories will not let us go until we tell them. Tell the story that is important to you. That is all that matters.

This, you know, is true.

So turn off the television, turn off your phone, take down all the pictures on the bulletin board. Except the one of your professor with the body of a sumo wrestler wearing a sombrero. After all, that one is art.

And find the article you cut out of the newspaper and put that up.

Natalie will stare back at you with fourteen-year-old eyes that hold more knowledge than they should.

Create a new document, find the distance, and begin.

Write in the second person. It's the trend now anyway, and you do not trust the declarative and are sick to death of the interrogative. Choose the imperative and take charge.

Begin with a young girl, a promising writer. Stay in the present tense when you describe how her eyes shine with excitement as she talks about *To Kill a Mockingbird*. From there, weave the tale of the English teacher who doesn't feel right about seeing her in Mr. Costa's room after school so much.

Put it all out there. Spend some time on the handsome History teacher. Tell how his door is always closed and one day you open it suddenly to ask him a question about progress reports and see him standing too close to Natalie. Remember how she did not meet your eyes. Start in the middle of things, that is, if you can find it. Remember the day you worked late and saw them in the darkness of the stairwell, the hushed whispers that sounded like fallen autumn leaves at your feet. You turned and went the other way. You said nothing because you did not know for sure. Even when her writing changed into something you did not recognize as Natalie. You know that we sometimes hide the story behind our words. Wonder if you were the only one who noticed her shell getting thinner. When her parents came in for Parents Night, remember your feeble attempt. What you say is cowardly and vague. Not surprisingly, her parents nod and tell you Natalie has always loved poetry. And finally, when, too late, you talk to the principal (you had to wait twenty minutes in the office for him to finish his conversation with the phys ed teacher, and while you listened to their easy laughter, you went over things in your head), words fail you then too, and he tells you these are dangerous accusations to make and you should not mention them to anyone else. Reveal subtly, through the subtext, his fear. Let the reader figure out, as you did, the motivation behind Mr. Costa's sudden "resignation" and the glowing letter of recommendation that followed him to his next job, this one at an all-girls school…

Don't stop there.

Accept the fact that there will never be enough psychic distance in the world for you to tell this part of the story. Tell it anyway.

Like everyone in town, you joined in the search for her. She had been missing for twelve hours, and each street was organized into search parties. Show, don't tell, how your group wove its way through the woods across from Whiskey Hill Road. It was early November and the autumn leaves crunched under your feet like hushed whispers. They were coated by a thin frosty layer, the first snowfall of the year, and the light was waning. You had just turned the clocks back and darkness crept quickly upon you; it did not help, this turning back of time. You would have needed weeks, months, not a single hour.

Tell how you saw her blond curls, almost blending into the frozen ground as the dusk gathered around you. You reached her first. The gun lay beside her outstretched hand, her curls spread out on the frozen ground like a geisha's fan.

It was cold by then and you were vaguely aware of your insides turning to ice, but you stayed there until the ambulance came. Don't look away. Keep the details vivid and precise as you tell how the coroner came and they zipped her into a black body bag. Some of her blond hair escaped and obstructed the zipper's path. The man's hands trembled as he tried to free the strands.

Tell that story.

Then hit send. Send it to your professor, and to the principal and to the Union president and to the local paper and to the police department. And to Natalie's parents. What the hell, go big or go home, and send it to *The New Yorker* and *The New York Times* and the *New York Post*. Send it out there. Send it everywhere.

Then wait.

Your professor will stare back at you from under that sombrero of wisdom, and in his knowing eyes, you will see a flash of approval. Hold onto it. You're going to need it. Because, at this point, the only thing you can be sure of is this: The phone is going to ring. The phone will definitely ring, and when it does…

Answer it.

ZEINA HASHEM BECK
Correcting My Mother's Essay

My mother started writing essays in English,
essays with wrong punctuation, wrong tenses,
wrong spacing wrong spelling,
with Arabic terms too, typed in English
(and a French accent)
when she cannot find
the translation for...*mina.*
In her e-mail she tells me

she's very "exited" about this—
her American teacher loves her ideas,
even in her bad English.
Their topic this week is "Now and Then,"
the teacher's given them two words:
"Boston   Marathon,"   asked
what it reminded them of.
My mom begins her essay by imagining

"the people who was about   to maratone,"
"how sad it is to be about to be running to your dying."
"Maybe they buy a new shoes yesterday," she writes,
"maybe they buy a new shoes for the maratone."
How sad, she knows, she knows how it feels like
"after you hear an explode,"
run to the phone
to check on your mother, your brother, your wife.

"Bad memories sleep," she writes, "but all of a suddenly,
all of a suddenly   they awake."
She remembers it now   that Friday.
How she walked to the pediatrician's
swinging me, three months old, from a basket
in her hand, my brother, five,

walking beside her.
She remembers his navy-blue clothes, his smile,
how the wind
"was taking his *blonde* hair straight aback."

She remembers the "suddenly explodes," the
"suddenly explodes,"
people running, cursing this country.
She remembers hiding
him in her jacket. "I couldn't breath,"
she writes, "I couldn't breath."
She remembers asking God
"to send all his angles! all his angles!"
to help her reach the building. She remembers
reaching the building in what felt
"like a worst century,"
finishing her own   "maratone."

She remembers watching
her "children   sleep   that night,"
"the sky red, intense, explosions."
She summons broken homes in her broken
English. "My hurt breaks today too," she writes,
"no matter where the killing is, my hurt breaks too."
She types it all in her fragmented English that I dare not

correct. Nothing is wrong with your broken English,
mom, nothing is wrong with your "Thanks God"
or the way you misspell "fiever" and "contry,"
the way you write "maingate"
instead of door. Nothing is wrong
mama, nothing, *mashi,*
with the way you "right"
"Allah ynajjina" instead of "God save us,"
you do not need to translate,
for we get it, *mama,* we get it
in every broken   language,
with every broken   heart.

MICHAEL HETTICH
The Windows

Everything's a window the professor told my class,
and I thought about breaking that glass, or shutting
the curtains, or better yet opening those windows
and climbing out into the snowy world beyond.
He said fashioning windows *is the only way*
we can make sense of what we see, so even
as I walked off through that snow I must have made windows.
Pretty soon I found a road, plowed clean and gleaming black,
between those walls of snow, and I walked, not the least bit
chilly, imagining I would find something
eventually. And pretty soon a big dog came bounding up.
I smelled wood smoke. Imagine discovering a village
full of people who seem to know you, at the end
of a long road, out in a wilderness of snow!
I stepped inside a house whose first floor was a dark bar,
warm and crowded with bearded men
who raised their glasses as I entered, beckoned me
to sit by the fire, and asked if I was having
the usual. I'd been lonely forever
I realized as the barmaid brought my soup and beer
with a wink that felt genuine. I was starving, so I ate
without stopping, through the night, and then I slept, in a room
with curtained windows behind which many birds
were singing, as though teaching me another way to wake.

NALINI JONES
At Mohanraj

Because my grandmother is dead
but because when she lived she favored this place,
I too have crossed the rutted road
and come to Mohanraj Jewellers.
At seven on a Sunday evening I could wire cash or purchase rubies.
I could change my dollars for a packet of bills the size of a grown
    man's shoe—
enough to buy shoes for all the barefoot workers who are digging up
    pipes or
burying them. The men let their mallets fall,
their shoulders jar like loose stone.
The women crowned with baskets of earth
spin, dreamy and grave, as if alone.

Their dance is never finished, the road never
finished. They dig ditches on the scars of ditches,
pits on ghost pits. This fresh hole is where I stumbled once
when I was young.
My grandmother caught me by the arm, my full weight snagged
between her fingers and thumb.
Beneath her soft flesh
I felt the points of her bones.

Tonight I carry my business in my pocket,
though here a woman wears what she owns. Gold cupolas
heavy as afternoon sleep, gold threads in her part,
gold songs at her ankles.
A narrow chiming breaks like water against her wrists.
Her babies are studded when their ears
are a milky dream of ears,
and the piercing quicker than pain.
One small soft cry she smiles to hear.

Inside the shop are clerks and clerks
as though a family could not stop producing sons.
None are Mohanraj himself
whom I will know by his silver mustache
and the great yellow coins of his eyes.
Perhaps he is also dead.
Perhaps he might have recognized me, for reasons of his own.
Perhaps he might have offered me a slightly better rate.
But the clerks are young and hurried. Their hands flick
like tongues to the mother of the bride,
spreading gold before her, quick as words.
Her fingers nibble at rings and chains,
another and another. No, her fingers say. Another.
She sweeps most away.
Beside her grows a tidy pile,
which in a little while, they'll weigh.

For that is the way at Mohanraj.
No one examines the chain I offer in trade, or the cross itself,
two thick limbs lashed by metal braid.
No one peers to see if the work is good, as you did long ago, that day
you held my arm and saved me. Something to last, something
to keep me safe. You looked and looked.
Now the cross and chain drop on the scale, a rattle like a breath of
    rain,
and nothing more to say.

Mohanraj appears as I am leaving, his coin eyes round as years,
and seeing me, Grandma, he asks for you by name.
Then he weighs the news, head tipping like a scale,
Yes, yes, so sad. But a long life, happy life. Hallo to Mummy.
Come back again.

It's always a matter of weight in the end,
what we save and what we cast away.
You walked these roads with your babies once.
You carried books, potatoes, chickens, prawns,
Eucharist for the housebound, sacks of rice,

letters from your children, grown and gone.
You carried sweet limes, which you peeled and fed me, chunk by
    chunk,
the plums for my pulao, my favorite
small bananas. You carried crosses in soft pouches, every trip another
cross, too many now to wear.
And I carry you, a small dry weight,
light as the necklace I have chosen,
filigree and filled with air.

LISA C. KRUEGER
Outside the Rialto

She is crushing on a younger guy after many conversations about things like the brain's musical notations or quinoa recipes. His round face, wire rims almost ubiquitous, every young man at work kind of looks like that. She tells her husband about the crush, he thinks it's probably good for her. When she talks to her crush she forgets to feel old. After a few weeks, she thinks maybe she loves him, not in an older-woman-stalking kind of way, but in a spiritual sense. Part of her just wants to be him, or wants him to be part of her. It feels harmless, the way they talk, laugh. When her crush dies unexpectedly, she plunges into a strange mourning. She doesn't cry, doesn't dream of him, however she begins to walk with a limp. Nothing hurts, her body just wants to limp, as though nursing a sprain. Her husband comes with her to the service. Standing-room only, a cacophony of hipsters, young families, matrons. Friend after friend goes forward to talk about his gardening groups, his Sunday afternoon mai tais, the concerts. Madonna, how the man loved Madonna. His mother cries, asking everyone to cherish his memory, the dad goes next and says some memories are bull. Divorced yet still they hug. Toward the end when the theater gets dusky and people shift around, shredding damp tissues, she feels overcome with a need to talk, to declare how beautiful he was to her, how she is learning to walk again. A woman near her speaks out, saying almost exactly what she wanted to say, using words she would have chosen. Outside the Rialto afternoon light crystallizes in prisms against the theater's deco façade. Her crush's partner is smoking, leaning against the pillars. He comments to everyone who passes, *This is my last one, I swear.*

No Damage

The sky was still dark when Trung Ngoc woke to a tap on her shoulder. She had been dreaming. In her dream, she was riding her brother's bicycle from her village in Vo Cuong to the nursing school in Hanoi. The endless dirt road and the heat had put her in a trance. When she felt the forceful tap, she had a momentary sensation of falling and tried to steady herself on the handlebar. Then she opened her eyes and realized she was in the employees' dormitory at Serenity Falls Nursing Home. She was not in Vo Cuong but in an industrial city in southern Taiwan. Someone was standing next to her bed. She reached for the bedside lamp but felt a hand grabbing her own.

"Don't wake the others up." It was the voice of Mrs. Lin, the on-site director at Serenity Falls. "Come with me. Something happened."

By the time Trung Ngoc had pulled herself up and was fumbling for her clothes, Mrs. Lin was already waiting outside. At the other end of the small bedroom, her two roommates grunted in their sleep. She put on her jeans in the dark, slipped into her flip-flops, and tiptoed out. As she followed Mrs. Lin down to the first floor, she saw the older woman's hands shaking.

They stopped at the medical room, where Mrs. Lin picked up a stretcher with both arms. As she turned around, the metal frame knocked on the desk. The thump startled them both, and Mrs. Lin let out a tiny scream.

"What happened?" Trung Ngoc asked.

"It's Grandma Liao. She couldn't unlock her thoughts."

Trung Ngoc wasn't sure what she meant, but the expression sounded vaguely sinister. Grandma Liao, one of Trung Ngoc's charges at Serenity Falls, had been in the quarantine ward on the seventh floor since Monday for a suspected case of tuberculosis.

"Should I get her ready?" In a state of confusion, she assumed that the test result had come back at four in the morning and the old lady was to be transferred to the medical center immediately.

Mrs. Lin didn't answer. Holding the stretcher, she waddled out of the office, but instead of heading to the elevator, she turned to the back garden.

The only source of light was the dim street lamp in a distance outside the brick wall. Trung Ngoc squinted to make out the pebbled path that cut across the lawn, and it took a while for her to see Grandma Liao's floral print pajamas, then she saw the blood. And only then did she realize that the old lady was sprawling on the ground, face-down, the upper half of her body on the path and the lower half on the grass.

"Dr. Wang is on his way," Mrs. Lin said. "But we need to clean this place up before everyone wakes up."

"What happened?" Trung Ngoc burst into tears.

Mrs. Lin placed the stretcher next to the body. She knelt down by the head and gestured for Trung Ngoc to lift the old lady's feet.

"I put her to bed last night." Trung Ngoc pulled up her T-shirt to wipe the tears from her face, almost scrubbing it. "She was coughing as usual, but everything was fine."

"You can cry later, but we need to clean up now."

Trung Ngoc placed her hands on the old lady's exposed calves. She had massaged those legs every day for the past three years to keep the blood flowing. She knew every brown spot, every bump, and every sinew on them; but now the extra fat under the skin felt like rice flour dough left out in the kitchen for too long. She picked up the legs as Mrs. Lin lifted the shoulders.

"Don't look at her face. It's not pretty." Mrs. Lin tilted the old lady's upper body. Together, they placed her on the stretcher.

They brought the body back to the doctor's office. Mrs. Lin was carrying most of the weight, with Trung Ngoc only lifting the other end of the stretcher so it wouldn't drag on the ground. She was careful with her steps so as to avoid the puddles from yesterday's rain.

"I don't think she suffered for too long," Mrs. Lin said once they put the body down. "I ran out as soon as I heard the noise. I am glad my room is so close to the garden. She was already gone when I found her."

"But she was fine yesterday. I told her she wouldn't have to stay on the seventh floor much longer. The test result was coming back soon."

"With these old folks, there's nothing you can do if they can't unlock their thoughts." Mrs. Lin sat down on the doctor's armchair, massaging her temples. She was a big-boned woman with thick arms, who could lift a grown man from a bed to a wheelchair all by herself. "The doctor will be here soon. No one else needs to know about this."

Trung Ngoc went back to the garden with a mop and a bucket of hot water. The sky was brighter now. Pools of blood and bits of pink matter were splattered on the ground, glistening under daylight. As soon as she poured the hot water over the pebbled path, she realized she had made a mistake. The blood had reacted to the heat and congealed into brown stains. She ran the mop over them back and forth, but they stuck as if having been imprinted on the ground. Its metallic smell grew stronger and stronger, mixed with odors of copper, rotten cabbage, and muddy rain water.

She picked up a hard bristle brush and a jar of bleach at the supply room. At the garden, she poured the entire contents of the jar over the grass and the pebbled path, then knelt down to scrub the stains. The noxious smell of the bleach permeated the air. After half an hour's work and several trips back to the faucet with the bucket, the ground was soaked with water, as if a tiny storm had just gone through.

Trung Ngoc didn't go back to bed but started her morning shift at seven, after a quick shower. Other than Grandma Liao, she had three more grandmas under her charge, all on the fourth floor. She went into each room, changed them out of their pajamas, lifted them onto their wheelchairs, washed their faces, brushed their teeth or fixed their dentures into their mouths, and blew their hair dry. By 8:30, she had comfortably installed all three old ladies in their wheelchairs and pushed them to their usual breakfast spot under a banyan tree in the back garden.

The day was sunny, though the heat in southern Taiwan had cooled down in November. The rain yesterday had damaged some of the azaleas along the brick wall, but the remaining ones were in full bloom. Trung Ngoc glanced at the other end of the garden and saw that the section of pebbled path that she had scrubbed so vigorously a few hours before was almost dry now.

She placed the breakfast—rice soup with shredded pork and kale—on the pop-up trays in front of the grandmas' wheelchairs and laid out spoons. She knelt down in front of the first one, fed her three spoonfuls of soup, then moved on to the next one. Since Grandma Liao had gone to the seventh floor, the conversation during their meals had been slow, and the old ladies seemed to get tired of each other's company quickly. Each one would talk to Trung Ngoc while she fed her. The conversation would be cut off abruptly when she moved on to the next old lady and would resume again when she came back, as if someone had pushed a "pause" button between them.

Today Grandma Meng was talking about either a soap opera or her husband. She had a speech impediment from a second stroke, and her tongue always got in the way. It took her about a minute to pronounce each word, but she never stopped trying.

"Hou-Houph," she huffed. "Huh-Huh—"

"All right, all right." Trung Ngoc patted her cheek. "We eat first, OK? We eat first, then we chat."

She sent two more spoonfuls of rice soup into the old lady's mouth and finally guessed correctly that she was saying "house." Then she turned to the next grandma.

Grandma Lee hardly ever spoke and often needed to be coaxed into eating. Trung Ngoc dug out a chunk of shredded pork and edged it toward her mouth.

"It has no taste," the old lady said. "I can't eat this if it has no taste."

"This is good for you. You don't want too much seasoning in your food. The salt and soy sauce'll shrivel up your skin and give you wrinkles."

The old lady sighed.

"So what is going on with Old Liao?" Grandma Ding at the next wheelchair asked. Her legs were weak from kidney failure, but she could still speak eloquently like the former department store saleswoman she had been. She didn't need to be fed except on the days before her biweekly dialysis. "When is she coming back? I'm tired of playing mahjong with that woman on the third floor. She's such a sore loser that we had to spend most of the game trying to let her win."

"They transferred her to the medical center this morning," Trung Ngoc said.

There was a collective gasp among them.

"Bud-phpi'ing—phpi'ing?" Grandma Meng struggled to squeeze out the words.

"So the test result came back?" Grandma Ding lowered her voice.

Trung Ngoc looked down at the bowl and didn't say anything.

"So it's TB, huh?" Grandma Ding said. "We call that blood-spitting plague here. But it's not that terrible. They'll fix her up real good in the hospital. It's not like before."

"How— How— Phu—" Grandma Meng said.

"When I was a little girl," Grandma Ding said ignoring her, "my aunt—that's an aunt by marriage, mind you; people in my family are clean and healthy—my aunt had the blood-spitting plague right after she had her first baby. She probably got it when she visited her own family in the countryside. That was right after the war, and we couldn't afford to send her to the doctor. So my uncle put her in a hut at the edge of the town. Us kids would look at her from a distance. Even back then I had enough sense not to get too close. She was always sitting out there on the porch and doing nothing but coughing and spitting out blood. We watched her disappear bit by bit."

"You should eat more," Trung Ngoc said. Grandma Ding had been stirring the soup with her spoon.

"Did the doctor say whether the TB's serious?"

"I don't know," Trung Ngoc said. "Stop playing with your food. It's getting cold."

"I'm fine," Grandma Ding said. "I'm not hungry."

"You're just going to eat junk food in your room if you don't have breakfast."

"What's that smell?" Grandma Ding said. "This place smells awful."

Grandma Meng grunted in agreement.

"It's probably the rain from yesterday," Trung Ngoc said. She shoved more soup into Grandma Lee's mouth. "They should clean up the leaves in the gutter."

She scooped up the third spoonful. The old lady shook her head but acquiesced after a little prodding. She smacked her lips together several times, as if trying to tease some taste out of the low-fat, low-sodium, high-fiber soup.

"This is disgusting," Grandma Lee said. "The stench is also killing my appetite."

"It's not the leaves," Grandma Ding said. "It smells like rotten meat."

"No, not rotten meat," Grandma Lee said. "When I was a child, we lived next to a butcher shop, and it smelled just like this."

"Did the kitchen just butcher a chicken?"

"When does the kitchen ever butcher a live chicken? The food might taste better if they had fresh meat."

The smell of rusted metal hit Trung Ngoc for a second, then it was gone. She looked in the direction of the pebbled path. She had cleaned up the garden so well last night that now she couldn't even remember where

Grandma Liao had lain. She sniffed again, and the smell came back, this time even sharper, mixed with rotten cabbage and muddy rainwater. It invaded her nostrils, and then even her lungs hurt. She looked at Grandma Lee, who was in no hurry to continue eating and gazed into the distance.

Stomach acid shot up to Trung Ngoc's throat, and she lurched over to the other end of the garden before she threw up into an azalea bush. All that came out was muddy yellow liquid.

Trung Ngoc knocked on Mrs. Lin's office door in the afternoon while the grandmas were taking naps. The on-site director waved her in and asked her to close the door.

"The grandmas know," she said.

Mrs. Lin looked up from her paperwork. "What did you tell them?"

"I didn't tell them anything. They smelled it. They said they smelled the blood, and I smelled it too."

"Maybe you need to clean up better."

"I cleaned up really well last night."

"Don't be a hysterical bug. Everything is fine now. The doctor signed the death certificate, and the family was very understanding. They agreed that it's best we keep everything quiet."

"Did they come and get her?"

"The people from the funeral home have taken her. They'll make her look nice again. The family was very kind, actually. They kept saying how sorry they were for the trouble and the shock. I told them they needn't worry. I had our best nursing attendant with me. I also told them how careful and how discreet you are. They were very grateful."

Mrs. Lin seemed to have slept little the night before too. Her eyelids were droopy, the skin on her face sagged, and the makeup, heavier than usual, accentuated the lines around her mouth.

"Did the test result come back?" Trung Ngoc asked.

"No, but it doesn't matter now, does it?"

"If she didn't have TB, she would have been up on the seventh floor for nothing. She was scared of staying there by herself. I told you I talked to her last night, but I lied. I had said I'd go up and talk to her every day, but I forgot because I was too tired yesterday."

"It's not your fault. Why don't you take tomorrow off? I'll get someone to fill in for you. It's not anyone's fault, and it's a good thing that no one had to be disturbed."

"I wish I had brought a TV up for her or something. I said I'd get her a TV, so she wouldn't be so bored all the time."

"It doesn't matter anymore. Grandma Liao is at peace now, and you shouldn't glue her to your heart."

Trung Ngoc slept in the next morning and spent the afternoon at the riverbank on the other side of the city. She often came here on weekends to browse through the boutiques, then she would go to a shopping mall nearby to buy cheap knockoffs of the clothes she had seen. On this weekday afternoon, however, most of the pedestrians were in suits and seemed to be in a hurry, and the outdoor cafés were empty. From the corner of her eye she saw a group of young men, sitting on the sidewalk, who looked like Thai laborers on leave from the steel factories. She avoided their gaze and walked on.

The river was a dull gray. Despite the clean mosaic-tiled sidewalk and the chic storefronts that lined the river, a stale smell of polluted water and mud wafted through the air. The newly planted ylang ylang trees were still too short and too sparse to provide any real shade, and the heat soon made her dizzy. She walked into a clothing shop that had air conditioning.

Everything inside was exquisite. The walls were painted in a soft, delicate pink; the air was cool and fresh; even the ample space between each hanger on the rack seemed deliberate. One corner of the shop exploded with things—an umbrella with lace trims and a mother-of-pearl handle, an end table with wrought-iron legs, ceramic bowls full of rings and little necklace charms on top of the table, hats hung on a hat rack, an overstuffed leather chair—while the other corner was luxuriously empty, with only a dress hung from a wooden ladder.

Trung Ngoc picked up the dress. It was light blue. The bodice was snug and covered in a layer of elaborate lace, and the satin skirt puffed out slightly. She looked at the price tag: 3,999 yuan. That was one semester's tuition for her little sister in Vo Cuong, who was also going to nursing school next year. A lace dress was not practical at all. She chuckled when she imagined herself in it while trying to bathe Grandma Meng. Perhaps she could wear it when she went back home next time, but her mother would only say she had wasted too much money and that just because she was working abroad didn't mean she was a rich girl. Besides, it would get dirty quickly from the dust and the mud on the dirt road in her village. She ran her fingers over the fabric. The lace was delicate and soft, and the color was a most precious powder blue. A knockoff would not look the same.

A young salesgirl, dressed in a frothy, pastel-colored chiffon skirt, approached with an awkward smile. She unfolded and folded a stack of T-shirts while eyeing Trung Ngoc. In Taiwan, she had gotten used to salespeople following her around, watching closely whenever she picked up anything. Usually, she would try to start a conversation with them, telling them how pretty she thought the shirt or the necklace was, to show that she spoke Mandarin. Sometimes she would tell them that she worked at a nursing home so they knew she had a real job and was not one of those mail-order brides living in the rural towns outside the city. Today she glared at the girl.

"I'm not going to take anything from your shop," she said and walked out.

She returned to Serenity Falls before dinnertime. She circled around the building and entered through the front gate to avoid the back garden, but as soon as she stepped into the lobby, the metallic smell of blood hit her. She stopped and held her breath for a few seconds. When she inhaled again, the smell became even stronger.

"Everything OK?" the pretty receptionist asked. She was looking at herself in a compact and getting ready to leave.

Before Trung Ngoc could answer, Mrs. Lin walked into the lobby with a wide smile on her face. "Here you are." She waved. "I was hoping you'd be back in time. Come with me."

Trung Ngoc followed. She constricted her throat to suppress the urge to throw up. After a while, she could almost ignore the smell.

A man and two women were waiting in the office. They looked to be in their forties, or perhaps in their fifties. She could never tell how old these Taiwanese were. The women were dressed in similar thin sweaters and well-pressed trousers, and the man looked tired and hot in a crumpled suit. They all had a small piece of white gauze pinned on their sleeves.

"This is our Ah-Ngoc I've been telling you about," Mrs. Lin said, putting one arm around Trung Ngoc's shoulders.

"You speak Mandarin?" the stouter of the two women asked.

Trung Ngoc nodded.

"She speaks perfect Mandarin!" Mrs. Lin said. "She understands

Taiwanese too. She watches all the Taiwanese soap operas with the grandmas and grandpas here. This is Grandma Liao's daughter." She introduced the stout woman. "And this is her son and daughter-in-law."

"I'm so sorry about all the trouble," the daughter said. "Mrs. Lin told us about the disturbance our mother has caused." She bowed slightly. The other two also bowed.

"No sorry, no sorry." Tears streamed down Trung Ngoc's cheeks.

In the three years that Grandma Liao had been under her care, this was the first time she had seen the old lady's children. She searched their faces. The son bore little resemblance to his mother, but the daughter had her square jaw and kind eyes.

"You must be the science teacher." She wiped away the tears with the back of her hand. "Grandma told me about you. She told me you teach at the best high school in Taipei, and you have a daughter who studies in America. She was always bragging about you."

The woman's face crumpled up into a demure frown that was exactly the same as the old lady's. Like her mother, she also had the habit of smiling apologetically as soon as the frown appeared.

"She was so proud of you all." Trung Ngoc turned to the son. "She told me you are an important lawyer and work for a big shipping company. She said the mayor was a guest at your wedding." She remembered the old lady's smile, the way it permeated her entire face when she boasted of her children. Tears were brimming in her eyes again.

"Oh." The son looked at his wife. She shrugged.

The daughter took out a red envelope from her purse and handed it to Trung Ngoc. "To wash away the gray fume."

Trung Ngoc didn't understand her and stared at the envelope without reaching for it.

"Bad luck," the son explained. "To get rid of the bad luck, to say thank you. You did a wonderful job. Thank you so much for taking care of the troubles."

"It was no trouble, and Grandma was not bad luck. She was a kind lady, a really, really good patient—my best one. She just got so lonely she couldn't stand it anymore."

"It's OK," Mrs. Lin patted her back. "It's OK. Ah-Ngoc takes care of her like her own grandmother. That's how we treat our residents here at Serenity Falls. But Ah-Ngoc, if you keep crying, Grandma Liao will be too worried about you to go to heaven."

The daughter took Trung Ngoc's hand and placed the red envelope in it. She felt it with her fingers. It was thick with cash. If those were hundred-yuan bills, it would be enough for perhaps only a semester's tuition for her little sister. Or ten crates of peanut stalks for her father's farm. Or that blue lace dress at the boutique. But respectable people wouldn't give small bills as present, and these people are very proper and polite. These must be thousand-yuan bills. At least thirty of them.

"Sometimes I wonder—I don't know if she's at peace. On the first day, when we said good night on the seventh floor, she kept saying it was OK. I knew it wasn't, but Grandma didn't want me to feel bad. When I visited the next morning, she looked terrible because she couldn't sleep. She told me she saw things." Trung Ngoc lowered her voice. "She heard them too. She was really scared and asked me to let her out. I had to say no. It was the doctor's order."

"Old folks can get carried away with their imagination sometimes," Mrs. Lin said, "especially when they have nothing to do all day. But that's all over. She's not scared now. She's up there and happy. I think she's having a good time in heaven playing mahjong with her old friends, and I bet she gets lots of pongs."

"She was happy *here*. She was everyone's favorite mahjong partner *here*."

"Yes," Mrs. Lin turned to Grandma Liao's children. "You know how difficult some of our grandmas and grandpas can be, but your mother had something nice to say to everyone."

"I don't know how her cough started," Trung Ngoc said. "I always make sure my grandmas are clean and warm."

"Of course you did," Mrs. Lin said. "You did a great job. It doesn't matter now."

Trung Ngoc knew she should stop talking. Having been in Taiwan for only three years, she couldn't understand everything other people said, but she could always detect the mood in the room, just as she knew instinctively if a grandma's or a grandpa's diaper was wet. She could tell if someone had just told a joke or made an argument, and she would laugh or nod accordingly. From the absentminded smile on the daughter's face and the son's sweaty forehead, she knew she should shut up.

"It's getting late," the daughter said. The three of them stood up and straightened their clothes.

"This wouldn't have happened if there were other people staying on the seventh floor." Trung Ngoc took hold of the daughter's hand, which was soft and substantial, a rich person's hand. "She pretended she wasn't coughing and her chest didn't hurt and begged me to take her downstairs. She cried and begged me. But I told her she had to stay until the test result came back. Only for a few more days. It was supposed to come back this week, the doctor said. Then she could go to the hospital or go back to the fourth floor. I said I'd find a TV for her so she wouldn't be so bored all the time. I just forgot. She was hearing those voices because she had no one to talk to. I said I'd visit every day, but I forgot that night because I was so tired. I'm sorry. You asked me to take care of Grandma, and I forgot about her. I lost her."

Trung Ngoc bowed her head and didn't dare to look at anyone in the room. No one spoke. Scent of perfume wafted in the air—either the daughter's or the daughter-in-law's. She couldn't describe it. It was not flower or fruit or spice. If anything, it just smelled expensive.

"Is this true?" the son finally said.

"Everything was done according to the regulation," Mrs. Lin said. "You are more than welcome to review the daily log." She detailed the management of the quarantine ward: morning bath and three meals delivered by the seventh-floor attendants, who had all been trained in the prevention of transmittable diseases, twice-daily visits from the nurses. But the daughter interrupted her.

"Ah-Ngoc said she forgot about her."

"She was not on duty at the seventh floor. The nurses—all nurses there are licensed professionals—saw her twice a day. Once at ten in the morning, and once at four in the afternoon, and all the stats were normal. Everything has been recorded in the log."

"Even so," the son said. "Clearly something went wrong."

"The management of the patients in the quarantine ward is stated clearly in the contract. I assume you read the contract when you signed it."

"It's not about the contract!" Trung Ngoc said, still clutching the daughter's hand. "She couldn't take it anymore because she kept everything inside. Everything. She asked me if you knew she was on the seventh floor. I said yes, because the contract said Mrs. Lin must tell you. She said you were all probably too busy to visit, because you're such important people, but she cried when she was alone.

Then she started hearing those voices. Please welcome her back to your home. When you pray for Grandma, please tell her you will look after her spirit now."

"We will do no such thing," the daughter-in-law said. This was the first time she spoke. Her voice was unnaturally high-pitched.

"Let's go." The daughter pulled her hand out of Trung Ngoc's and picked up her purse.

"No. These strangers here think my husband was a bad son and that you were a bad daughter. They don't know anything."

"I'm not a stranger," Trung Ngoc said. "I've known Grandma for three years."

"Then did she tell you that when my husband was a boy, she would beat him up black and blue when she came home drunk? Did she tell you that my husband still has nightmares about her? He's fifty-two, and he wakes up crying in the middle of the night. Did she tell you that?"

"It doesn't matter now," the son said. "It's all over. Stop talking, please. There's no need to show other people our ugly faces."

"People who don't know us should shut up." The daughter-in-law's thin frame hovered over Trung Ngoc, her narrow face so close to her that she could see the clump of mascara on the woman's eyelashes.

The daughter opened her mouth as if about to say something but only looked at her purse, put it down on the floor, picked it up, then dropped it again. The son dabbed his eyes with a blue checkered handkerchief.

"My husband had another sister. Did she tell you what happened to that one? And my sister-in-law here. Did that old woman tell you—"

The daughter walked toward the door, leaving her purse behind. Trung Ngoc rushed over and thrust the red envelope back into her hand.

"No, no, you must have it." The woman pushed it toward Trung Ngoc again, but she drew herself away. The woman then grabbed her arm and tried to tuck the envelope into her jean pocket. She patted Trung Ngoc's waist, almost jabbing her, as she searched for a spot to dispose of the cash. Trung Ngoc struggled to free herself, but the woman's grip was surprisingly strong, so she shoved her with all her force. That surprised them both, and they each took a step back.

"I don't want it."

"Please take it," the son said.

As Trung Ngoc turned her attention to him, the daughter grabbed her hand and shoved the envelope in it. Then she went to the other end of the office, almost jumped there, as if making sure she would never have to touch the money again.

"I'm sorry."

"There's nothing to be sorry about," the son said, then turned to Mrs. Lin. "I did read the contract. I remember it now."

"Yes," the daughter said. "I'm sure everything was done properly. There's no need to review the log. This is just a little bit of our hearts. It's nothing, really, compared to what you've done for us. We're grateful that you were able to handle everything so quietly."

"Yes, it's such a relief," the son said with a weak smile. He did resemble his mother after all, the way his thin lips were pressed tightly into a stiff upward arc.

The daughter-in-law glared at Trung Ngoc. Not speaking, she took her husband's arm.

"We should go." The daughter patted her hair and walked out without acknowledging anyone in the room. The other two followed. Trung Ngoc and Mrs. Lin remained a few steps behind them until they all stopped at the front gate.

"Thank you," the daughter said. "Please send the final bill to my usual address, and of course, if there's any damage, we'll be happy to—"

"There was no damage," Mrs. Lin said. "The ground has been cleaned up completely."

Trung Ngoc watched them turn at the end of the alley. The setting sun cast a purple hue behind the clouds.

"She told me he's very good-looking. She said when he was young, girls would wait for him at the corner of their street so they could catch him on his way to school. She always felt bad for them, so she would bring them scallion pancakes for breakfast. She said she still remembered those girls' names. But he's not good-looking, not even close."

"Maybe that's how she remembered him," Mrs. Lin said.

"She said her daughter would have gone to medical school if she had scored one point more in the college entrance exam. She married a doctor though, and that's better than being a doctor. That's what Grandma said."

"That sounds like her."

"I didn't know she had another daughter."

"I didn't, either." Mrs. Lin massaged her temples. "Let's not think about it anymore. Ah-Ngoc, you need to realize that every family has its own inscrutable prayer."

"I don't understand what you are saying. I need to go. I need to make sure my grandmas are eating their dinner."

LANCE LARSEN
Sad Jar of Atoms

Sad jar of atoms, I say when Jacqui cuts her thumb instead of a cucumber or returns from her run wet as a dog. *Sad jar* yourself, she says after a cop clocks me doing 45 in a school zone. This is called borrowing a Byronic phrase describing life and attaching it to your beloved. We've tried other terms of endearment. Vase of dolorous particles. Blue shot glass of unstable electrons. No go. Byron crackled with knowing, and possessed the kind of jar mopey girls in brocade dresses liked to touch in 1812. Once, carrying our baby at my hip, my sad jar dropped pickles in the parking lot. Being of limited means, we left the jar, but saved the pickles. This proves sad jars can be thrifty. A praying mantis is thrifty: watch it grab and tear much slower jars. A horse is a jar that contains too many gallops and neighs to count. Life is a jar of maybe, of who knows, whereby we grow older and bones turn brittle as hope. Some jars live a long time, like sea turtles, like Benjamin Franklin, a jar of genius filled with poor Richard and flirting in French and the desire to electrocute the earth using a kite and key in a rain storm. God is a jar containing all other jars—a nowhere and everywhere jar. Thy will be done: a jar of faith we whisper to the sky, hoping it will return with a message, like a homing pigeon. *A Love Supreme* by John Coltrane is a jar of licks that moves an audience to abandon one country of sad for a better one, all without a current passport. May all our jars be filled with lightning bugs, if not lightning. A poem is a jar made of sizzle and cordite. Crack it open in Greece and you'll find the wizened thumb of Sappho. Crack it open in Japan and you'll find a river and the eye of a bird, both moving, but at different rates of worship.

PHILIP LEVINE
Postcards

ALBA 1

8 a.m. and we punch out
and leave the place to our betters.
2,000 miles and fifty years
later and at my back I always
hear Chevy Gear & Axle
grinding the day shift workers
into antiquity.

ALBA 2

    The river works.
No one flips a switch, no one
shouts "Ready Set Go!" no one
writes a memo, it just runs
at its own sweet will its whole
blue-brown length toward six burned
lakes and seven seas.

ALBA 3

    The first
jackhammer breaks down
the dawn with its canticle
of progress. The garbage truck and
the street sweeper take their turns.
And the birds of the air and
the beasts of the field? They take
their lumps today and every day,
saith the TV.

The Angel Bernard

A gray row of corrugated huts
hunkering down in rain.
Across the way the fire burns
night and day though unseen
in sun light. Bernard wakens
to the aroma of warming milk
and burned coffee. Later we'll say
he had the bearing of an angel
with clear eyes, a wide brow,
thick golden curls. His mother,
home from the night shift,
prepares his day, so he rises
to stand on the cold linoleum.
Ford Rouge, where she works,
goes on burning and banging,
but neither notices. It's their life.
Nonsense, you say, how can the life
of an angel include a Ford plant
where new life is tortured
into things? You saw the girl Mary
in a rose gown shyly bowing
before a dazzling Gabriel, his pale
wings furled, this in an empty
church in Genoa the painting stained
but the scene unforgettable: That
was an angel bathed in his own light,
bearing the gift of a God, a presence
from another world. When Bernard
bows to dip bread in his coffee
his mother lays one hand down
on his bare nape as though she knows
he will die eleven years from now
in a fiery crash on US 24 on his way

to Dayton and thus leave his sons
behind. In this world the actual
occurs. In November the rain
streams skyward in cold sheets,
the fires burn unseen, the houses
bear down, separate and scared.

WAYNE MILLER
Inside the Book

For my daughter: these images,
these trenches of script. She keeps
reaching to pull them
from the page, as if the book
were an opened cabinet;

every time, the page
blocks her hand. They're *right
there*—those pictures
vivid as stained glass,
those tiny, inscrutable knots.

They hang in that space
where a world was built
in fits and erasures—she wants
to lift that world
into her own.

Meanwhile, *this* world
is flooding her thoughts,
her voice; it's filling
the windows, the streets
she moves through;

it's reaching into her
as the air reaches into her lungs.
Then, before we know it,
here she is with us
inside the book.

WAYNE MILLER
On Language

(for Jeanne)

1

There were only certain stones
                    we could step on to cross the river.

2

The stones we could step on to cross the river
                                were not certain.

3

It was difficult to decide if the stones were part of the river
or a scattered resistance to the river.

If the stones were form or content
                        inside the greater form of river.

4

Mainly the stones we stepped on
                        dropped away behind us
like the notes of a song.

5

A lovely village was there across the river—
but we spent most of our time focused on the stones.

When, finally, we arrived at the muddy bank, the village
had shifted impossibly
                              back across the river.

6

Love, stay with me inside this syntax of the river.

7

At times, the stones we stepped on
were at the bottom of the river. When we emerged—

our bodies no longer sails in the current—

the stones had risen
                              like balloons to the river's ceiling.

8

Those days, the river
                              filled our clothes, our ears, slicked us
like a dream.

9

We sat on the shoreline and looked back
across the river
                              we again would have to cross.

Looking, too, was a form of crossing.

10

Inside the forever-descending current of the river
was a countermoving archipelago of stones.

11

Stones that, we discovered, crossed the river.

12

We spent our days crossing and crossing the river.

MICHAEL MORSE

Void and Compensation (Migraine)

for Allen Grossman

Here's a side effect that's very front and center:
I am forgetting the words for things. It's not a matter

of mistaking the Ash for the Linden, of conjuring
the chickadees to my hand from the Arrowwood.

They are a certain kind of medicine like the image
of the beech leaves moving in a wind I cannot hear.

My head-hurt, that crush of pebbles in a tin pan,
it's still for the moment—but not my forgetting.

That's closer to home—opaque and gauzy-drunk.
There is a bowl in the dish drain; it has holes in it.

I use it to wash the greens that come out of the ground.
I use it to let water run away.

What do you call that drain inside the other drain?
Words arrive like spores from other worlds tried on and out.

And although I talk to myself like snow
in evergreens or blackbirds on wires

I know not what I'm looking through to see—
This help I need, in deed, in trust—what is it called?

I'm reading a poet who is building a boat for his death—
in love with his fading mind and what he has left of it.

It is inside his head and looks out at stones
on a beach and remembers his mother, ideas

like a chest and some ribs and something
plush and heaving in that space, ideas

like God and heaven-hell winds that come here
to move the birch and beech leaves, then remove them.

LEX RUNCIMAN
It Doesn't Look Like Much Now, Does It?

Current face, new domino in the mirror,
it doesn't look like much now, does it?
Has anyone seen the infant?
Because of course the infant cannot speak.
Has anyone seen the week of early March,

1962, origin of the scar on this chin, scar
thinned now and the chin short-whiskered.
Trying to slide on concrete into home—
that wish made a long abrasion, ripped
trousers, and opened a ridge of bone

that shocked Kelty—the O of his mouth,
and caused Mary Earp to scream,
and caused the man who was my father at work
to be called—which he hated—to take for stitches,
four of them, this clumsy, enthusiastic, unsteady

boy, whoever he was.
Has anybody seen the 1960 yellow-finned Chevy,
last reported steaming north, head gasket blown,
no remedy but water and stop, water and stop.
Mostly the past doesn't look like much now.

Little bits sparkle. You want to isolate
that afternoon sun shone on the hail,
and several nights (who's counting?), and dinners
in good company. You want to slow, replay, enjoy,
and sharpen that moveable blur parenting made.

The past doesn't look like much now, now,
this moment slipping away, this moment a neighbor's
plastic resin chair rests white on its curved side—

the odds of this or any of us so impossible
I say not *miracle* but *what the hell.*

SHEROD SANTOS

J.

The smell of her on the book she left behind, the taped tear in the dust
    jacket,
        the neatly printed marginal notes,
the dog-ears, check marks, underlinings (single and double),
    the phonetic
        spelling of the Russian names
on the inside of the back cover. Setting it aside I wondered if I had
    seen too much,
        more than she might've liked me to,
more than I might've liked as well, for when she later asked if I'd
    enjoyed the book,
        I responded in purely literary terms.
Though I went on pretending nothing had happened, I couldn't
    escape the impression
        that I too had been marked
and deciphered and underscored; that even my deepest secrets had
    been subject
        to her claims as a reader.
But what if she'd read me incorrectly? Or worse, what if, all along,
        she'd only taken me literally?
What if she'd never looked me in the eyes and seen me for who I am?

LAURIE SEWALL
White Lake Breaking

Love, if you want me
to speak, let me find

a way out of my sadness.
You are everywhere

lingering—moss over rock,
rock over seed, seedlings

about to remember. I
recall you in small

things and nothing: stones
upon water—water

turned hard, into rock.
Here on the listening lake

things burn to be born
and then buried—seed

into pond, pond
into withering light. Words

cannot move into this—let me
break open to you, not

in my sound but yours:
egg out of stone, moss

out of light, white
lake breaking open to fire.

MAIREAD SMALL STAID
Better

Life, the devil you know, the one
you've bantered, bartered with,
trading this day for that, this love
for that freedom, that freedom back
for happiness. Something lacking,
something gained. The devil
is one hell of an investor, turning
a profit continuous as flames.
You are wood. You are the paper
you signed your life to in exchange
for this sweet spate of days. This
is the deal you've made: he lets you
hold years between your fists, gripped
as steering wheel & gear shift
on an empty road. He lets you go—
so fast, so far—before the dark
renders you irrelevant, a child
sent to bed while the party goes on
below. Before he hands you over
to his brother, the other devil, the one
you don't.

LAURA VAN PROOYEN
Lineage Fragment

She taught the girl how to roll dough thin, but Frances
didn't teach me. I was too wild

to crimp a crust. Once, in a fit, I took off my shoe,
raised it above my head, but never meant to throw it.

A stranger at the post office recognized someone's face
in my face, noted I must be near

to Frances. Said I must be part of the bouquet. I didn't know
any bloom beyond lilacs, except for violets

scattered in the grass. I couldn't see then
where my face belonged. I didn't know my cheekbone

was 100 years old, or that my smile
wasn't mine, or that my eyes creased in laughter were extinct.

LAURA VAN PROOYEN
Frances of the Cadillac

Under her tongue, there was a story.
In her mouth, nails. Frances hammered license plates
to the back wall of her garage. There

hang the years that sunk like a foot in loose soil.
That rusted like a hinge. Whose hand or what machine
etched the numbers that cruised along

in the exhaust of a town that no longer exists?
This is what happens when I check my wristwatch.

Frances drives her leather-topped Cadillac
between the electrical signals of my brain. There's
a railroad crossing, and I don't understand

the way she's looking at me. Her body says something
happened. Her arms so thin, the veins visible
when she rolls up her sleeves. Still, if I were drowning

I know Frances would save me. She might throw
a string of black pearls. She might offer a broom handle,
worn from her sweeping. She'd pull me to the edge,

push pennies from my lungs. But it's the bells
of the crossing that make me unable to breathe.

MATTHEW VOLLMER
This World Is Not Your Home

The town where you grew up—the place you'll always think of as home—has three stoplights, a grocery store, a twin cinema, a post office, two dozen churches, three banks, a hospital, a handful of gas stations, and three factories that produce custom wood furniture, Lee jeans, and outboard motors. There's a main street where teenagers drive Mustangs and Chevys on Friday nights, a parking lot where they raise hoods and rev engines. There's a video store with a Spy Hunter arcade game and rows of VHS boxes featuring bare-chested, bazooka-wielding hunks, flanked by brunettes in wet T-shirts. There's a Happy Flounder whose checkout counter offers a box of Fruit Stripe gum and a canister of Lion Mints. There's a rec center with a public pool and basketball goals netted with chains. There's a barbershop where old men tell stories about bear, coons, huckleberries, railroads, gardens, and the dearth or surfeit of rain. There are hot, gleaming tracks where oncoming engines flatten pennies to glossy oblongs. There are mountains—blue ridges rising above the town like the walls of a distant citadel. There are woods where you find Jack-in-the-Pulpit and Lady Slippers and puffballs that, when squeezed, ejaculate greenish smoke. There are snakes and wasps and hog wallers, secret waterfalls and caves where outlaws once hid. There are fields whose dirt, when plowed, surrenders pottery shards, musket balls, and arrowheads: the artifacts of a Cherokee civilization whose members, three centuries ago—before Andrew Jackson signed the Indian Removal Act of 1830, and before said Indians were rounded up and marched, at bayonet point, from cool, hemlock-shaded hollows to blistering Oklahoman prairies—would've outnumbered the white people living here now.

You're one of those people, and you've lived here your whole life. Even so, when you're biking down Main Street—on your sky-blue Schwinn Predator, the one with the pegs and the silver rotator cuff that allows the handlebars to spin—you feel conspicuous. Maybe it's because you don't really live *in* town but on its outskirts, in a cove at the base of a mountain. Maybe it's because you know so few town folk, while your dad—a dentist—can't go anywhere without someone stopping him to give him a hard time about hardly working and thus embarking upon the kind of banter in which two people engage one another in mutual but affable disparagement. Maybe it's because your family belongs to a church whose members gather together to worship on the seventh day of the week instead of the first—a church that views itself as separate from the rest of the world. Maybe it's because your best friends are a pair of sisters—a freckled blonde named Jolene, a brunette named Raylene—who live in a house on Happy Top with a trampoline and rabbit cages and a plastic clown head in the yard, which, when hooked up to a hose, shoots water out of its skull. Maybe it's because you don't go to your hometown's public elementary school; instead, you meet five other kids in the parking lot of the Valley Plaza every morning to carpool to another town, to a private church school in a three-room A-frame house. There thirty kids in grades one through eight gather to learn about the walls of Jericho, the scepter of Herod, the Ark of the Covenant, the faith of the Centurion, and the Spirit of Prophecy, which was made manifest over a hundred years ago within a young woman named Ellen Gould White, who also happened to be one of the founders of your church, a girl who, when she was nine years old, was struck in the head with a rock, took ill, and never fully recovered, though at seventeen, she shouted "Glory! Glory!" and was granted the first of many visions: people walked on a narrow pathway of light toward heaven; those who kept their eyes upon the illuminated body of Christ could walk without stumbling, while those who looked at their feet fell into the dark.

The year is 1985. You stand four feet ten inches tall. Your father thinks you should part your hair; you prefer, out of habit, to comb your bangs over your eyebrows. You have a dent in your chest—the scientific term is *pectus excavatum*—that makes you self-conscious; when swimming you insist on wearing a shirt. You have a scar on your leg where, while showing off some karate moves to a friend, you simultaneously kicked and lunged, plunging the tip of a Swiss Army knife straight through your jeans and opening up a mouth of fatty tissue in your thigh—a perforation that your father sewed shut using thread he uses to stitch holes in the mouths of his patients. You wear a shirt your mother stitched together out of fabric imprinted with tuxedoed penguins, or a gray hooded sweatshirt with a black mesh crop top emblazoned with the words "Dallas" and "Cowboys." You think of yourself as fast and elusive, and though you can't play football on a team for real because your family observes the Sabbath from Friday sundown to Saturday sundown, you dream of being so good that you'll bypass high school and college and sign a contract with the Cowboys as a walk-on, and that your athleticism will be so valued by your coaches they won't require you to attend Saturday practices.

On May 25, 1985, you'll be eleven years old.

You may live in the boonies—at the end of a dirt road at the bottom of a mountain, in a house on a mossy, molehill-ridden hump above two streams—but thanks to TV and *Sports Illustrated* and *Time* magazine and *People* and Walmart and Casey Kasem's Top 40, you're into the usual stuff. *MAD* magazine. The NFL. Michael Jackson. Rich Little. Sticks shaped like guns. Fighter jets. Ninjas. You tie T-shirts around your head, knotting the sleeves so that the head-hole stretches tight across your eyes. You fashion a pair of homemade nunchucks by sawing a broom handle in half and nailing a strip of chain to the ends. You check out a how-to book on ninjutsu from the Nantahala Regional Library that illustrates stealth tactics, including grabbing onto a gutter spout while walking up the side of a house. You check this book out again. You renew it. You dream of actual Chinese throwing stars. Of blowguns. Of swashbuckling rooftop fights during which you employ dual samurai swords to disarm your enemies.

Your younger sister likes to dress up in your mom's old heels and your dead great-aunt Maddie's mothbally dresses. Your mother bakes her own bread, makes clothes using a sewing machine, cross-stitches pictures of African American men eating watermelon, plays the piano for church, and runs a fundraising program for your school that involves selling boxes of oranges and grapefruit ("the citrus program," she calls it) to locals. Meanwhile, your father—a balding man with glasses, who strikes you as simultaneously nerdy and robust—spends his days staring into mouths: fleshscapes of rotting bone, where incomprehensibly strong tongues, coated with mucous-thick yellow plaque, lap involuntarily against his rubber-gloved fingers, like quick blind slugs.

You enter your father's office with a sense of propriety: it's a place you might inherit, assuming you, too, become a dentist (which seems as likely an occupation as any), a place where you can come and go and do as you please. You press the square, colored buttons on the X-ray machine, commandeer a vacant dental chair and make it rise and fall by depressing a pedal, squirt the walls or the inside of your mouth with the water hose, create a mobile indentation in the flesh of your hand by spraying it with the air gun, ride the wheeled chairs of the receptionists' area, and rummage through the treasure box, keeping the best erasers and stickers for yourself. You play with a hinged set of oversize fake teeth (ostensibly used by hygienists to model good brushing, though you've never witnessed them do this), take inventory of the refrigerator in the lab where your dad torches clay models of his patients' teeth and where his assistants often eat lunch or stir squishy green bowls of acidic-smelling impression mixture, pour yourself a Dixie cup of Diet Coke, or—best of all—flip through the channels on the little TV, which has cable. You don't have cable at home—the lines don't come out that far, plus your mother thinks you watch enough junk as it is—and so visiting the office inevitably involves watching TV, usually TBS, which means episodes of *I Dream of Jeannie* and *Bewitched,* both of which, with their benevolent sorceresses, might've been argued by your elementary school teacher to glorify and therefore make safe the idea of witchcraft. You don't worry about that, though. You like the idea of magic being real. You'd like to have your own genie. You wouldn't waste a single wish.

Your family calls your father's employees "the girls." You like the girls. The girls are locals who obtained degrees at Western Carolina or Tri-County. The girls watch soap operas and visit tanning beds and drink diet soda. They play practical jokes on each other—leaving rubber snakes in file cabinet drawers, shooting fellow staff members with water guns on their birthdays. They bring leftover cake and leave it in the lab and Lord, yes, get yourself a piece. On Halloween, the girls dress up as tubes of toothpaste or Pippi Longstocking. Every year, they present you with a birthday cake on a foiled mat from the local grocery store: Superman, Spiderman, Bugs Bunny, Snoopy. One of the girls— a white-haired woman whose husband recently retired from the railroad and now watches Cincinnati Reds games via satellite, in a room where he is surrounded by memorabilia sheathed in plastic—sells Avon and routinely gives you cologne and shampoo in bottles shaped like cowboys and footballs.

Your father's patients—ex-Olympians, ex-cons, massage therapists, farmers, teachers, real estate agents, mechanics, bank tellers, prisoners in leg-irons, drug addicts, mail carriers, covert marijuana farmers, pharmacists, overalled millionaires who own land-clearing companies— call him "Doc" or "Jim," pronouncing these words "Dawk" or "Jee-um." You remember them and you don't. In the summer, they bring sacks of tomatoes and okra and corn and potatoes. Jars of honey. Venison jerky. Knives with pearlescent handles. Jellied rhubarb in jars with stickered lids that record dates of canning in scrawling cursive. There's Homer, a one-eared man, who carries a bear vagina in his wallet. There's Munk— a raspy, bald-headed slab of a man, who has a larynx that grinds words into hamburger. There's the wife of a pharmacist who owned, for a brief period of time, a gift store that sold sculptures of medieval villages. There's Kandi, the town poet and real estate agent, with whom you remember being enamored as a kid, partly because her name made you think of sweets and partly because a sheet of brunette hair fell down her back. There's Judy, the bank teller who's never been caught without makeup, not even when she mows her lawn or crawls into bed for the night. And there's Robert—a ruddy, big-cheeked, pot-bellied man who rides a moped and mows the office lawn, and who claims to be the cousin of Xavier Roberts, the inventor of the Cabbage Patch Dolls. Robert has proposed on many occasions that he can get your family into Babyland General Hospital—in nearby Cleveland, Georgia— whenever you want. At Babyland General Hospital visitors can view a room where dolls emerge face first from the center of flaps of green fabric that have been sewn to resemble cabbages. The idea of a fake hospital intrigues you, but you hate dolls, especially these, with their squishy heads and adoption papers. You prefer Garbage Pail Kids: a cast of grotesque cartoon babies with names that seem lifted from some forbidden playground song: chubby-faced kids smoking cigarettes, barfing up blocks and live goldfish, crawling half-decomposed out of graves, wielding machine guns and sticks of dynamite, emerging from toilets. Garbage Pail Kids have names like "Unzipped Zack"—who unzips his face to reveal a grinning skull—"Armpit Britt"—a bikini'd gal proudly displaying yarn-thick tendrils of armpit hair—and "Hy Gene"—a lil' dude with a five o'clock shadow who razors a strip of flesh (it curls like a jagged apple peel) from his face. You probably shouldn't delight in these images—what would Jesus think?—but you do.

*

Nineteen eighty-five is the Year of the DeLorean, and of those twin infinity symbols that signify an exit from the present, into the past, back to the future: 88. In 1985, the top NFL quarterbacks sport short-longs, and basketball players wear short shorts. A white-bearded country singer is considered "hot." The journalist Terry Anderson is taken hostage in Lebanon. Johnny Carson jokes about the Ayatollah and Gorbechev. TVs advertise ATT and Pepto and Metamucil and Grape Nuts and WrestleMania and Sanka and Beautyrest mattresses. Kids play Atari. Nancy Reagan consults a psychic. Women wear blazers and shoulder pads and bracelets that resemble gold CDs. The best NBA player is a dorky-looking white guy with a mustache. Mr. T plays a bad ass who's terrified to board a plane. Madonna's big eyebrows don't diminish her allure. Michael Jackson—his face sculpted but not yet grotesque—appears in magazines wearing aviator sunglasses, military-style jackets with epaulets, and the white sequined glove. He writes a song with Quincy Jones and sings it in a studio with a group of stars that includes Tina Turner, Bruce Springsteen, Willie Nelson, Billy Joel, Ray Charles, Smokey Robinson, Bette Midler, La Toya Jackson, Cyndi Lauper, Dionne Warwick, and Diana Ross. You hear this song on the radio of the carpool moms that allow rock music (in other words, everybody but yours). "We are the world," they sing, and though you and your friends think their earnestness is cheesy, you sing along with them.

If you thought about it, you'd have to admit: this is not a song you should be singing. You've been told—and more or less believe—that this world is not your home. That you're just passing through. Your treasures? Those are laid up beyond the blue. So it's not really right for you to lift your voice in unison with people who are saying that "we" are the "world."

What you believe: you are and you aren't.

Sometimes, after school, you go home with the sisters—with Jolene and Raylene—to jump on their trampoline. One day, somebody gets an idea: "Let's shout bad words while we bounce!" You won't remember what the sisters yelled because their words didn't make sense—they weren't words you knew. You'll only remember the word you yelled:

the S word. Andrew Mintz—a tall, uncoordinated kid who took up most of the backseat during carpool—used to trick you into saying it, by asking you to say "it" after he said, "sh." Raylene, though. She upped the ante. She yelled the F word. At the time, you had no idea what the F word meant. You'd never heard it before. As you jumped, leaping higher into the air, you yelled your respective bad words at the top of your lungs, as if they might help you fly. You yelled until your throats burned and your eyes watered. Then the sisters' mom—a joyful, freckly woman whose affection for other children was unappeasable and unabashed, a woman who used sliced veggie wieners as a pizza topping and let you crank up Air Supply and Kenny Loggins on the way to school and bought you soft serve cones at Micky D's when she picked you up after—heard you and ordered everybody inside. The sisters went to their respective rooms, decorated with unicorn figurines, miniature Smurfs, and wicker basket-seats that dangled from the ceiling. You sat in the living room, worried yourself sick while sitting at an ancient piano whose keys were chipped and yellow, like a set of bad teeth, listening to the sisters howl as their mom spanked them. Later, the mom came into the living room and softly said, "Do you know what that word means?"

You shrugged.

"Do you know what making love is?"

"Yes," you said, even though you didn't, just thought you did, thought you knew what love was, though if she'd pressed you and said, no, not love, MAKING love, you would've faltered, not knowing love was something that could be made, could be manufactured, figured it occurred naturally, but she didn't press you, just said, "That's what the word means. It means when two people make love," which confused you, because you thought she'd been talking about the S word, and you'd always thought the S word was a word for defecation, a word your grandmother used, *defecate* for the S word and *void* or *micturate* for the P word. Later, your dad picked you up in his truck and took you home, and on the way, he told you the truth about how people were made. It flabbergasted you. You'd heard plenty about people in the Bible praying for children and then God giving them babies. You'd thought that was how it worked: a baby was the result of passing a test, having faith. And now you knew it was just like Raylene had said, out by the rabbit cages: that the male bunny sticks his penis in the female bunny, and a little while later, baby bunnies come out.

*

On May 25 you will—finally, officially—be old enough to be baptized. It's a day you look forward to. You want to be a member of your church, which believes that the dead aren't really dead but merely sleeping, and that the rest of Christendom has forgotten the fourth commandment, which is "to remember the seventh day is the Sabbath of the Lord thy God," and that in the future the members of your church will be persecuted for not worshipping on Sunday, but that soon afterward Jesus Christ will return and ferry those who have been steadfast to heaven. You want, during Communion Sabbaths, to make your younger sister envious by reaching for a thimble-size glass of grape juice resting in a silver tray, to take a wedge of unleavened bread and chew it thoughtfully with your eyes closed. You are not, however, that crazy about participating in the Ordinance of Humility, during which you'll be called upon to retrieve a towel and a silver basin of water to wash the feet of another male parishioner. You pray that you'll be able to wash your father's feet. You'll peel his sock from his foot—an opaque, white appendage veined with blue—and slosh water between his toes, noting the patches of hair on the knuckles. You'll eyeball the lint sloshing in the basin. You'll thank God you don't have to wash the feet of other men, whose calves have been imprinted with elastic, and whose toenails are thick and yellow.

On Thursdays, a balding, mustachioed man—a pastor from Michigan who likes to listen to sad country music and calls ice cream cones "cones a' cream"—visits your home. Every week, in preparation for your baptism, you read and complete one of a series of blue booklets in a folder titled "Baptismal Study Guide." The series begins with a questionnaire titled "Spiritual Need Evaluation." It instructs the respondent—in this case, you—to read each question, then circle a letter between A and E, "A" signifying one's "highest interest" and "E" one's lowest. You circle As for "Do you think Jesus will come in your lifetime?" and "Would you be embarrassed if you were asked to pray in a classroom?" and "Do you feel forgiven after you've prayed for forgiveness?" and "Does the Sabbath do anything positive in your life?" and "Do you enjoy the Sabbath?" and "Are you comfortable answering the question: Why are you a Seventh-day Adventist?" and "Do you feel that you are important to the church?"

and "Do you feel that the Bible is a help to you in your daily living?" and "Do you understand what the Bible is saying about salvation?" and "Do you find the sermons you hear interesting and helpful?" and "Do you get anything out of going to church?" You circled Bs for "Do you enjoy reading the Bible?" and "Do you find the counsel of Ellen White helpful in your life?" and "Do you talk to your parents about spiritual things?" You circle a C for "Do you feel that prayer makes a difference in your life?" You circle no Ds, but Es for "Have you read any of Ellen White's books other than those required for classes?" and "Do you talk to your friends about spiritual problems?"

The booklets tell stories: one relates the story about a man offering to take another man's punishment in a concentration camp. Another relates the story about a Papua New Guinea tribal chief who had a dream in which he was told to lead his people to another group of people who worshipped on the seventh day and he did and now his entire village belongs to the Seventh-day Adventist church. A booklet titled "The Trinity" begins with a story about triplets. A "Think on This!" section asks readers to consider the "fact" that it takes more faith to believe in evolution than creation. The "Discussion and Reaction" part of "The Nature of Man," instructs the reader to "draw a simple picture of how you think you will look in your glorified, eternal condition, or list the things you would like to do in heaven as a first, second, and third choice." Yours are: "Fly," "See God," and "Visit Space." In "The Great Controversy" booklet, you learn that "From the beginning of the conflict the entire universe has looked on with interest as Satan has made his charges against God." The "Jesus Christ" section begins with the story of an imposter Christ. In "The Remnant and Its Mission" Discussion and Reaction section," No. 3 says "I must be careful that I do not feel superior to other Christians because I have been given special understanding about the last special message for the world before Jesus comes. What are some of the ways we might feel superior, and how might I express them?"

You don't know how to answer this question.

You leave it blank.

In your father's office, you are summoned to examination rooms. His patients can't believe how much you've grown. They say things like, "You probably don't even remember me." And you don't. Not really. You feel known by people in the way the child of a celebrity might be known by the public: you—who exist largely within the private realms of church, church school, and your home—are often recognized, but ultimately unknown.

Your father moves effortlessly among his fellow citizens: in hardware stores, pharmacies, supermarkets, gas stations, the post office and barber shop. He buys chainsaw grease. Gloves. Kerosene. Coca-Cola in glass bottles. A haircut and neck shave from a six foot six barber named Jack, a WWII vet who isn't afraid to declare that he knows for a fact the Japanese have submarines parked beneath the city of Los Angeles.

Once a year, he camps with a band of local men. They load jeeps and camper-topped Fords and Chevys with tents and sleeping bags and stoves and coolers of food and ascend to the tops of the highest ridges, where they hike balds of whispering mountain grass and gather blackberries in plastic pails. These men, like your father, boast thickly muscled hands. They do not work out. Aside from coon and deer and boar and turkey hunting, they play no sport. They don't give your father a hard time about his religion. They know when his church day is and respect him for having one. They dip fingers into Skoal tins and tobacco pouches. They spit into bottles or cans or between their feet as they rest elbows on knees. They wear camouflage, overalls, mesh caps with the word CAT in yellow letters. They say "ain't never" and "they law" and "good Lord" and "shoot." They light cigarettes, blow smoke in dual plumes from their nostrils. Black lines rim their fingernails. One year, somebody slides a *Playboy* into the sack of a man—tall, strong, overalled, head-quivering—who cannot read or write, can't sign his own name, who has never kissed or danced or held hands with a woman, and—from a distance—watches him turn the pages.

On your birthday, you stare into churning water: the waist-high pool where your body will be lowered and your spirit transformed. You know miles of this creek by heart; you can see it in your head. There's the pool where you caught your first fish using a line baited with a corn kernel, and there's where you took the butt end of a Buck knife and thwacked the head of a rainbow trout, and held onto the slick, thrashing body, trying to avoid the sharp undersides of its scales. There's the falls where you've thrust your head, where the frigid roar took away your breath, causing you to remember how, according to your father, an overheated farmer had flung himself into a pool as cold as this, and the subsequent shock stopped his heart. There's the giant boulders where you've surveyed the creek's most dangerous turn and where the water slows and deepens, lapping against a rock wall that bears—like an indecipherable inscription—a series of wavy lines indicating eons of water levels. There's the pool your father threw you into when you'd sat on a yellow jacket's nest. There's the place where, while he was chain-sawing limbs, you fell and broke your arm and, at first, he ignored you because you cried when you fell into creeks, even when you didn't get hurt.

You don't believe baptism will save you—that is, you don't believe, as you know many people in your town do, that "once saved" means "always saved." Nobody in your church does. And yet: here you are. You are wearing a robe and tennis shoes as you wade into the stream. The water's frigid. But the pastor's not shivering. Behind him, a froth of white bubbles. The pastor says the magic words—"I now baptize you in the name of the Father, the Son, and the Holy Spirit"—and places a handkerchief over your mouth. He lowers you backward into the stream. You go under; you rise up. A chorus of *Amens* follows. Church members sing. You're cold. The robe clings to your body. A fire blazes inside a makeshift pit your father built on a rock ledge. Sunlight flashes between cracks in rhododendron leaves. The people on the other side of the creek, the old women in folding chairs, the old men in their button-down shirts, your mother with her camera, your sister, your friends, are singing a hymn whose name or tune you won't remember. You'll know this is special, that nobody else has ever been baptized in this pool, but you don't feel any different. No shaft of light descends from heaven. No warmth floods your body. You know there are two of you: the you before the baptism and the you after. But—aside from having experienced the event—you can't tell the difference. If you've been transformed, you can't feel it. You think maybe you're changed. That now you'll finish your Sabbath School lessons each week, that you'll be nicer to your sister. You hope you will. You worry you won't.

It—this non-transformation—is a secret that you keep from your father, whose eyes water when he stands before the pulpit as a deacon calling for the offertory; and from your mother, who plays piano with perfect posture; and from your sister, who fails to register—at least for now—as a person in whom you could ever confide; and from your uncle, who's a member of a famous Adventist singing group; and from your other uncle, who will one day become president of the world church; and from your grandmothers, one of whom you've never heard utter a harsh word about anyone and the other who worries that when she worries, she's committing a grievous sin; and from your grandfathers, one of whom had been a beloved physician who had helped free a concentration camp during World War II and the other—a dentist whose last three fingers on his left hand had been cut off, down to the first knuckle, by his older sister when he was three and she was six—who likes to think of himself, whenever he has occasion to ride a horse, as a cowboy. More significantly, it's a secret you keep from yourself because you're afraid of what it might mean: that, in the end, you might not be who you say you are.

You'll get plenty of chances to pretend. Next year, you attend summer camp—the "Tween" division, for 12-year-olds—in the rolling hills of north Georgia. You use a bow to shoot arrows at targets pinned to haystacks in a hot, gnat-ridden field. You drop from a rope swing into a lake, line up for roll call, visit "Ma" and "Pa" at the "Mountain Lore" cabin, and watch Chad—a long-haired skateboarder—make out with Angela: the prettiest, tannest, blondest girl at camp.

On Saturday, you're sitting in church—a carpeted gymnasium—when, at the end of the sermon, a minister, standing at a pulpit beneath a basketball goal, asks the crowd—boys sitting on one side, girls on the other—a question. "Is there anyone here who wants to give their hearts to Jesus, to renew their lives for him? If so, would that person like to come forward, to the altar?" You hear the rustle of church bulletins, of dresses, of tennis shoes scuffing the gym carpet, but nobody rises. Not at first. Not your friend Tom—a kid who wears Husky jeans and sleeps on hospital beds during his mom's night shifts at Murphy Medical—and not your friend Chris—a kid who lives with two brothers and a sister in a single-wide trailer on Hardscrabble Road in Mineral Bluff, Georgia, and who seems happiest when engaging in acts of subversion: flipping people the bird when no adults are looking, bragging about smoking rabbit tobacco. "Surely," the pastor says, his voice now booming through the microphone, "there's somebody here who wants to rededicate his or her life." Nobody rises. Not your friends. Not your enemies. Not the kid who brought the Guns N' Roses shirt. Not the kid who wears three pairs of striped athletic socks at once. Not Chad.

Not Angela. The pastor calls again. And again: nothing. Nobody. You wonder how long he can go on. You fear you might be stuck here forever. You don't hear a voice saying *Go* or *Come* or *Now*. Even so, you rise from your chair. Your heartbeat works your blood into a coursing storm. You're shaking, but you walk down the aisle. You sense a stirring in the room. Every eye's focused on you.

At the pulpit, the pastor asks your name. You tell him, and he shouts it like an example: as if you're the embodiment of that which he'd been seeking. Another kid rises and comes forward. Others follow. Twos. Threes. Entire rows. A hundred preteens, illuminated by fluorescent lights, swarm forward. You fidget. You avoid their eyes, brimming now with sincerity, and wonder if the ones who stay in their seats—including Tom and Chris—think you're a phony, and you wonder if now you'll have to act different. Be different. That people will expect more of you, and you won't know how to deliver. Most of all, you already feel guilty because, as much as you'd like to say that you did it for Jesus, your motivation was singular: to stop the calling. But don't admit that. Don't even think it. Tell yourself that God called you forward. Remind yourself that His eye is on the sparrow, and so how much more is it on you?

One of the sisters from Happy Top winks at you; it's like you're a celebrity and a long lost pal is employing a secret signal to say hello. The piano has started. You're all singing "Pass It On," the lyrics of which you'll never forget: "It only takes a spark, to get a fire going, and soon all those around, can warm up to its glowing. That's how it is with God's love." So true, you think, despite the fact that you've never told anyone about God's love—at least not anyone who didn't already know. But maybe you will. Maybe, this is some kind of a turning point. You hope so. You won't want to be one of the ones who, in the near future, turns his face heavenward to watch as an everyday, run-of-the-mill cloud in the distance unscrolls to reveal itself as a mass of otherworldly fire and subsequently feels his eyeballs explode into flames. No. You'll want that light to bathe you like balm. Because that light won't be earthly fire: it'll be a spaceship made of angels and horses and rainbows and a throne upon which the Savior sits, the whole mass barreling toward Earth like a massive vacuum cleaner, sucking the righteous dead from their graves and the righteous living from the cliffs and crags to which they'll be clinging, a stream of righteous souls gathering at the heart of a pulsing vessel, so as to escape the now-blazing pandemonium and fly somewhere far beyond the blue.

It's not only that you don't want to get burned alive with the rest of the wicked.

It's that everyone you love will be flying away forever.

And you don't want to get left behind.

You don't want to die.

So you sing.

Loud and clear.

Meet me in heaven.

Pray that we all will be there.

And here's the magical part: when you're singing, when your chest thrums with the reverberations, you have no doubts. The song is a sweetness, a foretaste of glory, a balm that allows you to feel—at least for the duration of the song—as if maybe the stories you've been told your whole life are true, and that now, today, you have been healed and made new.

AFAA MICHAEL WEAVER
Space

I think myself thin until
a scale calls me to honesty,
its numbers the mind of God,
unrelenting, and I question
a machine that can drive us
to uncertainty, to suicide,
or into the edges of murder,
thinking we are more or less
not there or here. One day
I walked down a street feeling
myself there, feeling as thick
or thin as I wanted to be, light
suddenly a web of shadows made
by utility wires, trees, lines
connecting houses to houses,
as if purpose itself is a thing
we have to assemble, a puzzle
with keys in lives we lived
in other worlds. We have
no weight on those days,
we make no impression
in this world, wherever it is.
I was there as I am here
in what we dream or imagine
ourselves to be, our voices
coming to nothing in a planet
untamed by hallelujahs.

GARY YOUNG

"In the woods..."

In the woods, hunting mushrooms, I saw a flash of white, and thought Amanita, Death Cap, but it was just a piece of paper. When I picked it up, I recognized my own handwriting. It was a note I must have written months before and dropped. Waterlogged and half-eaten by slugs, the ink was faded, but I could read, *the willingness to use our minds is what erodes our minds.*

GARY YOUNG
"Five ravens climbed..."

Five ravens climbed a redwood, hopping from one limb to another. They could have flown to the top of the tree, but they took their time, and stopped to preen before jumping to the next branch. The woodpeckers, who'd hectored the ravens all morning, sat in another tree and watched the ravens as they made their slow ascent. It's difficult to be honest with yourself; that's why it's good to have an adversary.

EMERGING WRITER'S CONTEST WINNER
FICTION

In fiction, our winner is **Tomiko M. Breland**, for her story "Rosalee Carrasco."

Ploughshares' fiction editor Margot Livesey writes: "In the elegantly structured 'Rosalee Carrasco,' Tomiko Breland describes the before and after, as well as the actual events, of a very particular day at middle school. The voice is elegant, empathetic, and vivid without ever being obtrusive, and the narrative moves with impeccable timing from character to character. I was full of admiration for the intelligence of the story, and for the restraint."

Tomiko Breland grew up in Monterey, California, with an early hunger for writing borne under the auspices of Roald Dahl and Madeline L'Engle, Jules Verne, and C. S. Lewis. In her writing, she is interested in pushing the boundaries of form in order to test the boundaries of emotion. She received her BA in English from Stanford University and her MA in fiction writing from the Johns Hopkins University. Tomiko's fiction placed in the 2014 Writer's Digest Popular Fiction Contest, and she is currently completing her first novel.

About the piece, Tomiko writes, "In novel writing, you have the space to give the reader the past, present, and future of many characters. I challenged myself to find a way to do the same in the form of a short story without the traditional use of flashbacks. The format came first, and then the story sort of poured itself into the form."

TOMIKO M. BRELAND
Rosalee Carrasco

I

When Charlotte was very small, she played a game called Pretty Pretty Princess with her older sisters, and she never once won. One of them always became the prettiest princess, draped in pink or blue or purple plastic beads and a shiny plastic crown.

At eight, she was accepted into the circle of Ashlee, Tabatha, and Danielle, and even though they said to her *You're not as pretty as us, but we'll let you play with us anyway,* Charlotte conceded to their haughty governance with fawning displays of appreciation, and unmitigated devotion and loyalty.

In sixth grade, Charlotte fell in love with Scotty Marlowe. She sat behind him in geography class and mapped the spattering of copper freckles on the back of his neck instead of the primary-colored countries on the blackboard.

Yesterday, Danielle helped her narrow down her dress choice for the eighth-grade dance to a silver number with a conservative neckline and a sexier, asymmetrical piece in "oasis blue." Charlotte was leaning toward the blue dress.

II

The four girls are the last to finish getting dressed after second period phys ed class. They are always the last to get dressed because they take their time reapplying fragranced lotion to their ivory limbs; glinting baubles to their discriminating wrists and ears; and expensive, shimmering makeup to their delicate eyelids and lips. Ms. McCreary knows this, so she leaves them to finish preening while she prepares the gym for the next class. Mr. Pickert, their pervy third-period algebra teacher, knows this, but what Ms. McCreary calls "tardy," the girls call "fashionably late," and Mr. Pickert calls "reasonably delayed," as long as they sit in the front row with their long legs emerging from short skirts. Rosalee Carrasco knows this, which is why she chooses this specific time to step into the girls' locker room at Oak View Middle School and reach into the pink, rhinestoned messenger bag at her side. *What do* you *want, skank?* Ashlee says, looking up, holding a comb with its teeth paused in her straightened, tawny hair. Rosalee pulls out a semiautomatic Smith & Wesson 40 VE. It is heavier in her hand than when she fingered it this morning in her father's desk drawer. She points the cold black barrel at Ashlee.

III

Tomorrow, Charlotte will stay home from school, where she will lock herself in her bathroom and scrape under her fingernails with a toothpick, and then a metal nail file, and then a little Swiss Army knife. She will struggle to get the blood out from under her nails until the blood that is there is her own.

She will stay home for the remainder of the school year, and she won't answer calls from her friends. Her older sisters will bring her homework from school, and they'll help her complete it on the floor of her bedroom. One of them will show her how to equalize a basic equation while the other kneels behind her, brushing her hair.

When the new school year begins, Charlotte will attend high school in a new district, where nobody asks her questions.

In fifteen years, she will marry a quiet young professor from UC Berkeley, and they will have two daughters.

When they are old enough, she will tell them that they are both the prettiest princess, even though they never ask, and even though she doesn't believe it.

I

At just five years old, Ashlee's parents bought her a Shetland pony.

Her mother went to college with James Dewitt, Danielle's father, and this is how Ashlee and Danielle became inseparable.

Ashlee was always second in command because her parents were not as rich as Danielle's (her father moved around real estate, while Danielle's father moved around stocks) and because her mother was half Black, though they never spoke of it.

When other little girls asked to play with them, Ashlee laughed.

She played tennis—but only indoors because she'd learned that too much sun was costly.

It was Ashlee who noticed, last week, that the Mexican girl had begun her period and didn't know it. She had a blossom of dark red on the back of her khaki pants. Ashlee pointed it out to the others. Someone (not her, certainly), took a picture with his or her camera phone, and posted the picture on Facebook, tagging everyone in the school.

II

Rosalee is nervous and angry and she doesn't know what she's doing. She planned this, and she planned what she wanted to say and how she would say it, but she hasn't thought past that. She just wants them to listen to her, to be scared, to feel what it feels like to be powerless. She wants a lot of things. Tabatha takes a step toward a locker, and there's no exit but the one Rosalee is standing in, but Rosalee says *Sit the fuck down* anyway. Danielle stands up and repeats what Ashlee said, without the epithet, and much more calmly: *What do you want?* She stands in a little rectangle of morning sunlight thrown into the room by the small, high windows above the lockers. It puts her perfect face half in shadow. Her hair is perfect and her clothes are perfect, and she was in the middle of doing her makeup, so only her bottom lip is shiny with gloss. She seems in control, even when she's not. Rosalee hates her for this. Rosalee's hand is trembling, the heavy black and silver Smith & Wesson is trembling, and when she speaks, her voice is trembling. She releases the safety, the way the YouTube video showed her. *I want you to pay,* she says.

III

Tomorrow, Ashlee will go to school. Reporters will sneak onto campus, and one will pop out of a bush like a gangly bird of prey and surprise her. He'll poke a mic in her face and ask if she knew Rosalee was crazy. She'll say, *I didn't think she was crazy. I didn't think about her at all.*

She will stay friends with what remains of her clique through high school, but there will be something off kilter, as if the shifting of elements within the group has thrown off their center of gravity. She will feel the subtle prick of exclusion when her father loses his real estate job in yet another recession, and after high school, they'll lose touch completely.

In college, Ashlee will stop lightening her hair, and she will experiment with a new drug called Chastity. Things will unravel rapidly. She will drop out of school, and huge chunks of her life will later appear as empty spheres, or as bleary shapes viewed through a glass of water. It will take twenty years for her to clean herself up, and she will, in therapy, retrace it all back to that day in the locker room at Oak View Middle School. She won't go any further than that.

I

Tabatha was born in October. She was a Libra.

At two years old, Tabatha would not stop eating her crayons, and her mother had to remove all crayon and crayonlike objects from the house.

Her little brother was born when she was five, and when he was two months old, she pinched his nose closed while he slept to see him open his little pink, translucent lips like a fish. Then she kissed him.

When she was six, she gained an appreciation for the proper use of crayons, and turned out to be a capable artist.

In fourth grade, she and her three new friends helped her dad paint a mural with an ocean theme on the wall in her little brother's room.

When she was twelve, she was her brother's hero.

Tabatha Roth was also in love with Scotty Marlowe.

Yesterday, like every Tuesday for the past 15 years, Tabatha allowed herself to chew gently on a crayon when nobody was looking, before she went to sleep. She liked the feel of wax between her teeth. This crayon color was called "blush."

II

Do you want money? Danielle asks. *We can give you money.* Rosalee is confused for a moment, knits her brow. *I don't want your fucking charity.* She's never cussed this much, and the word *fuck* feels powerful in her mouth. She says it out loud again, just for good measure: *Fuck.* Charlotte, with her reddish curls bouncing irreverently, moves behind Tabatha. Danielle says, coolly, *Well then, what do you want?* And she crosses her arms like she's not scared, like nothing in the whole world scares her. She learned this from her father, who has always told her that "People are cowards, but Dewitts show no fear." Rosalee feels that she's losing control of the situation, so she aims at the ceiling. The girls all raise their arms and cover their heads with their hands, instinctually, as Rosalee pulls the trigger, which is harder to squeeze than she'd anticipated. She expects the bullet to strike the plaster tiles and cause a shower of white powder to rain down on them, instilling fear. But instead, it makes a sharp *ping* on a pipe, and it's several seconds before anyone notices that Tabatha is no longer standing. She is an awkward heap on the floor.

III

I

Ms. Janet McCreary was born on a small farm in Pennsylvania, where she milked goats and reveled in lightning storms from her upstairs bedroom window. She saw lightning strike the lone Striped Maple in the center of a field beneath her window twelve times.

She was a highly precocious child, and she read hungrily, consuming books under her blankets with a flashlight well after her mother turned the lights off. She and her friends spent their time talking about boys and books, but more often books.

Ms. McCreary studied German lit in college but found afterward that her skills were not very marketable. She began teaching P.E. until she found a position more suited to her.

She met her fiancé, Matthew Parker, on Match.com. Within a year, they'd determined the location and the guest list for their wedding. It would be in June.

Three weeks ago, Ms. McCreary, with much happiness, told her fiancé that she was pregnant. She rigged a game of Scrabble by hiding tiles under the table, and played words like *baby, father,* and *family* until he caught on. He was elated.

II

Ms. McCreary hears the shot from out in the gym, but it doesn't register with her what it is. This is only a middle school, and she has never heard a real gunshot before. She moves unhurriedly toward the locker room, annoyed with the four girls she left there: What have they done now? As she turns into the locker room, she sees Rosalee from behind. She can see the girls on the ground beyond Rosalee and wonders what they're playing at. *Strange,* she thinks. *Danielle Dewitt is on her knees.* It is then that she sees the gun. She thinks *Scheisse,* because she always curses in German. Ms. McCreary doesn't know what to do. Her instinct is to talk to the girl, but she hesitates—maybe she should try to subdue her, or go call for help. Her eyes flicker to Rosalee's right, where she's certain she left a softball bat leaning against the wall. She takes a step closer, and she can hear Charlotte on the ground mumbling something over and over, but she can't make out what it is. She takes another step, but stops, and raises her hand silently to her stomach. Charlotte moves her hand from Tabatha's head to her own and touches her temple, leaving a bright smudge like a child's red finger paint. She is saying, *She's dead, she's dead, she's dead.*

III

Tomorrow, Ms. McCreary will spend much of the day in the police station, giving statements. She will be tired, but more than that she will be afraid she's going to lose her job because she is never supposed to leave kids in the locker room alone. There was death on her watch.

Despite the fact that there were more students in the gym who required supervision than there were in the locker room, Ms. McCreary will be the scapegoat for Ella County School District, and she will lose her job.

In two weeks, she will have an abortion, and she will tell her fiancé that it was a miscarriage. She will tell herself she finds unbearable the thought of bringing a child into a world where things like this happened, where her children would have to play and learn and live—with children *like this*.

In one year, her fiancé will leave her, and she will let him.

In six years, Ms. McCreary will relocate to Germany, where she will teach English and begin writing. She will publish an article titled "Social Violence and Accountability in American Literature" in a modest academic journal.

I

When Rosalee Carrasco is born to a French mother and Chilean father, she is crying.

Rosalee is always doing and going and performing. She is always trying, and learning.

When she is six, she is feeding her two younger brothers mashed bananas with a tiny rubber-coated spoon because her parents work overtime to pay for her private school.

When she is eight, she is buying trendy pink bracelets and standing nervously in line next to Ashlee at lunch. She is viciously ignored.

At nine, her mother is scolding: *Enfant ingrat! You have nothing to cry about.*

When she is seven and eight and ten and twelve, she is asking *Can I play?*

At thirteen, she is falling in love with Scotty Marlowe. At thirteen, she is understanding.

At fourteen, she is watching herself become a woman in the mirror, and then she is watching herself become a woman on Facebook, and then she is watching the custodian pull dark, bloody tampons from her locker with gloved hands. She is cowering as boys call her "Rosa-leaky."

II

Rosalee, honey. Ms. McCreary says, her voice hardly above a whisper. Rosalee whips around, the gun pointed at chest level, both hands wrapped around the grip. She's been holding it up for only a minute, maybe two, but it feels as if she's been holding it her whole life, and it is heavy. Her eyes are big and round as quarters, and Ms. McCreary can see the whites all the way around her dark pupils. Behind her, all of the girls are huddled around Tabatha's body, and one of the girls—Charlotte—is sniffling. *Rosalee,* Ms. McCreary says again. She steps toward the slight girl, whose dark hair is pulled severely behind her head, making her look older than she is, and whose fear makes her look younger than she is. The teacher holds out her hand, slowly, slowly, her palm up. It is the universal sign for *Give me the gun.* The barrel begins to drop, slowly, slowly. Danielle stands suddenly and says, *She killed Tabatha* in a voice that is a sob and an accusation and a taunt; it is all of these things. *I didn't,* Rosalee cries out. Her words come out high and hollow; they echo without resonance. She spins around wildly, points the gun at Danielle, and Ms. McCreary shouts, *Rosalee!*

III

Rosalee will be charged with five counts. She will be convicted of three counts, and she will serve four years at a juvenile correctional facility, where she will read Sylvia Plath and ZZ Packer, and keep to herself.

When she is released, she will go to community college, where she will major in women's studies. She will become interested in acting, and join a small troupe at a local theater.

She will be quiet and withdrawn, dark and inscrutable. Men will fall in love with her, or rather, they will try to fall in love with her, but she will not let them. People will try to get close to her, but she will push them away.

In her most acclaimed performance, she will star in the role of Wendy, in Peter Pan. She will be most convincing when she plays Old Wendy and her young daughter Jane asks her what it is she sees in the darkness. *Nothing*, Wendy says. *Yes*, counters Jane. *You see when you were a little girl.* And Rosalee says, *That is a long time ago, sweetheart.*

For the rest of her life, she will be always doing and going and performing. She will be always remembering.

I

Danielle Dewitt was a happy, occasionally colicky baby.

Her older half-sister Sophia dressed her up in cashmere and anointed her with makeup when Danielle was four; she looked like a painted porcelain doll.

When she was five, her older half-brother Colin taught her how to fish. She caught a small salmon and threw it back, horrified.

At Mimi's Finishing School for Children, she learned how to read a French dinner menu. At home, she learned how to read people, how to put herself at the advantage.

When she was nine, she stole her sister's beloved diamond stud earrings and flushed them down the toilet.

She considered herself a good, charitable person; she made her father donate to the whales every Christmas.

Last week she conceived of and forced the girls to carry out the prank on the Mexican girl. Danielle said that each girl had to supply an "item" so that none could be exempted if they got caught, except for Tabatha, because Tabatha was a virgin and so hadn't begun using tampons yet. She, however, acted as lookout.

II

Danielle, who had stood up and stepped forward a moment ago, made brave by the presence of an adult, steps back again. The barrel of the gun is shaking wildly in Rosalee's hand; if she pulls the trigger, the bullet could fall harmlessly wide, or it could hit Danielle right between her pretty blue eyes, a fatal blemish above her straight, narrow nose. Rosalee says, *I didn't kill her, it was an accident,* and behind her Ms. McCreary is nodding her head, *Yes, yes. Of course it was.* Rosalee says to Danielle, motioning with the silver barrel, *Tell her. Tell her it was an accident.* And Danielle says, *It was* while she's exhaling, so they can hardly hear her. *And tell her,* Rosalee says. *Tell her what you did to me.* Danielle's eyes flit, imperceptibly, to Ms. McCreary and then back to Rosalee. *We didn't do anything to you.* Rosalee moves suddenly toward Danielle, the gun at her side. Ms. McCreary is yelling something in the background, but neither girl hears. Rosalee steps up to Danielle, so close their noses are almost touching. They are breathing each other's heavy breaths. Something passes between them: an expression, a quivering of the pupil, an exchange of molecules? Rosalee drops the gun.

III

Danielle will go to school tomorrow and she will dazzle before the paparazzi. She will be quoted as saying, "I never even spoke to the poor girl before this. She must have been obsessed with us."

She will go to the eighth grade dance with Scotty Marlowe, and she will look stunning in a slinky, asymmetrical dress that is "oasis blue."

She will use what she'll refer to as "the Tragedy" to get her father to buy her a Hermès Birkin bag, then a Mercedes C-Class when she turns sixteen, and then a shopping trip to Paris at eighteen.

She will go to Sarah Lawrence University, marry a dermatologist, and have three children by Cesarean section before she is thirty-five.

She will read *Charlotte's Web* and *James and the Giant Peach* to her children when they are small, and they will bicker for her affection.

One day, just before her youngest daughter begins high school, Danielle will hire a maid named Rosa. She will pause for a moment as she cuts the stem off the bottom of a tulip, and she will think that maybe she knew someone once by that name.

In nonfiction, our winner is **Eliese Colette Goldbach**, for her essay "In the Memory of the Living."

Ploughshares' editor-in-chief, Ladette Randolph, writes that the essay "is a haunting meditation from the far shores of addiction, mental illness, and obsession. Eliese Goldbach movingly chronicles her journey from sheltered girl to damaged woman through her obsession with the tragic death of the elusive 'Possum,' which acts as both evidence of her downfall and as a pathway out of self-destruction."

Eliese Colette Goldbach attended the Northeast Ohio Master of Fine Arts Program, and her work has appeared in *Western Humanities Review, Southern California Review,* and *Slipstream,* among other publications. She lives in Cleveland, Ohio, where she is currently working on an essay collection that examines the effects of trauma on identity. "Much of my writing examines identity in the context of bipolar disorder and memory loss," she writes. "I'm interested in the life of a mind prone to extremes.

About the piece, Goldbach writes: "Obsession became a driving element of this particular essay. Obsession as unchecked action and uncontrolled thought. Addictions and fixations and manias. Obsession as intrusion. Obsession as unruly imagination. My research was obsessive. My rewrites were obsessive. I drafted and redrafted the essay as a love story, as an "other woman" story, as a mental illness story. I drafted it as a revenge story, a recovery story. In some ways, the essay has retained all of these elements, but it is perhaps more a story of salvage, which always implies a loss."

ELIESE COLETTE GOLDBACH
In the Memory of the Living

His wife called herself Possum. He often had nightmares that she was only playing dead.

One night, he jolted awake and scanned the room.

What's wrong? I asked.

Nothing, he said. *Just some crazy dreams.*

Later that day, he smoked Maverick 100s at the kitchen table while I washed dishes.

I had this nightmare, he said.

About what?

I dreamt that my Ex-Old-Lady was only pretending to be dead so she could sabotage me.

Smoke twisted from the digits of his left hand where the word SEXY had been tattooed in a melting font.

My Ex-Old-Lady. That's mostly what he called her. Sometimes *My Ex-Wife.* Sometimes *That Hateful Bitch.*

He never said her name. Not even a mention of the nickname Possum.

He called me his Old Lady after Possum's death, but I was not old. And I was never his wife.

His wife died of a heroin overdose in the bathroom of a Greyhound bus.

I met him while working a summer job at a painting company.

I was twenty-two and inexperienced. He was twenty-eight and married.

I dismissed him as *taken.* He was out of my league anyway with his dirty blond hair and blue eyes. He could wear a Fedora without looking a fool, and he'd eaten the best taco of his life outside a whorehouse in Tijuana. He'd walked over coral reefs in San Diego, and he'd driven across the country while drinking Beam and beer. I figured he couldn't possibly be attracted to a sheltered girl who once said, "I love Bruce Springfield," while listening to "Born in the U.S.A."

But he flirted with me at the company camping trip. His wife hadn't come. They were on the outs, so he spent his time fetching me beers and lighting my cigarettes. It had been raining for days. The grass had become mud. Everyone else huddled beneath a pavilion, trying to stay dry.

Let's walk, he said, and I followed him.

We wandered until mud coated my calves.

While walking down a narrow path, we came across a sign that read, *Church in the Woods.* A semicircle of tree trunks had been laid out as makeshift pews. A wooden altar stood beneath the dripping leaves of oaks and pines.

We climbed the altar and looked out at an empty congregation. He kissed me beneath the storm, which was already moving east. The altar creaked under our shifting feet. When he reached a hand beneath my shirt, I balked. After all, he was a married man.

But your wife, I said, stopping his hand on my stomach.

We're in the process of getting divorced, he said. *She just has to sign some papers.*

You can put your hand up my shirt when you show me the papers.

At the end of the camping weekend, I gave him my number. I checked my phone constantly, waiting for a copy of the divorce papers.

He never called. They never divorced.

I couldn't compete with a wife named Possum.

He met Possum in high school, but it wasn't until years later—when they shared a nitrous balloon at a party—that they got together. He asked her out for a date of thrift-store shopping and Scattergories. She eventually moved into his house and got them both jobs at an escort service—he drove the girls around while she answered the phones. Eventually, the cops raided their house and charged them with compelling slavery. A friend bailed her out. He sat in jail.

They split up after that, and they stayed apart for seven years. When he contacted her again, it was winter. He picked her up at night. "That first glance I got of her as she walked through my headlights," he wrote in a journal, "her beautiful green eyes that perfectly contrasted with her vintage orange coat lined with fur. She looked amazing. The very instant we got inside my apartment, I kissed her."

They married shortly after that night, on March 24, 2006.

That was their relationship. Fierce or nothing—like the Valentine's

Day he bought her Champagne, even though they couldn't afford it. One of them picked a fight, and he threw the Champagne bottle out the window. Jagged glass clung to the frame. The bottle landed somewhere in the bushes. She called the police, claiming that he'd aimed for her body. *He was trying to kill me,* she said. *I feared for my life.* The police cuffed him and took him to jail, where she bailed him out with the rent money. They were left with nothing more than an empty bottle, a broken window, and his freedom.

It was Possum who got him hooked on heroin.

"Things were good for a brief time," he wrote about their relationship, "but then came an excess of drugs. Although I'd tried heroin [by the time we met], I really didn't connect with it. [...] It would all end badly."

Before the heroin, he'd been earning a degree in physics. He had vague notions of becoming an eccentric professor with disheveled hair and Velcro tennis shoes. But school got dropped. And family got dropped. And he found himself ripping off quick-cash marts to fund his habit.

Once, when they were moving out of a house in California, he handed her a bag full of used syringes and empty dope bags. *Throw these away,* he said. It was the one instruction he gave her, but she was too high to follow through. When the cops pulled them over, the bag was in the back of the van. He claimed the syringes were all his and went to jail. She came to visit. Drool dripped from the corners of her mouth. She kept nodding off. *There's no bail money,* she said. He blew up, edgy from detox. *You're fucking high right now, aren't you?* She threw back her head, opening her eyes a little wider. *No, no, I'm not high.*

Their life together was one of breakups and detoxes. Reunions and relapses. They'd disappear into the heroin where they didn't want to eat or shower or fuck. For six years, every emotion—sorrow and elation— diluted in their veins. It was a forced amnesia.

Much of my own memory has been erased.

During the years he spent shooting heroin with his wife, I suffered incessant bouts of mania and depression. I'd seen doctors. I'd been to hospitals. I'd taken medications. Nothing seemed to help.

In the year of his wife's death, I was hospitalized in the psychiatric ward six times. I thought the devil was inside me. Occasionally, I'd dip my finger into a bottle of antifreeze and bring it to my lips, acclimating myself to the taste of suicide.

During my fifth stay in the hospital, a doctor recommended electroconvulsive therapy. He explained the risks. Grogginess. Headaches. Perhaps a bit of memory loss, but nothing that couldn't be recovered. The whole process was touted as a miracle treatment—few side effects with maximum effectiveness—so I signed the informed-consent papers.

Halfway through the treatments, my memories began to dwindle. I forgot how to get to the grocery store. I forgot the plots of books and movies I'd seen and read. I forgot what I'd done the previous day and the previous year. Every time a friend said, *remember that time when…*, I shook my head. My recollections were all black. When people persisted (*my god, how can you not remember that time?*), I'd lie. I'd pretend my memory had just surfaced. *Oh, yes, of course I remember.*

My memory was the only thing that went. The depression remained. The mania remained. I still found myself in hysterical fits, writing suicide letters and loading my father's antique Remington rifle.

But I never objected to the treatments.

Every electroconvulsive treatment was the same. I dressed in a hospital gown and brown booties. A nurse stuck me with the IV, the doctor rolled in a blue box that emitted the necessary shock, and the anesthesiologist pushed Brevital Sodium—an anesthetic used to induce brief periods of unconsciousness—into my veins.

Goooood niiiiight, the anesthesiologist said as she unloaded the syringe.

For a few seconds, the lights grew gauzy. My body tingled and warmed, as if the seat of myself were thawing into vapor. It was always at this moment that I desperately fought sleep. I tried to keep my eyes open. I tried to breathe more deeply. I wanted to remain in that melting state where the rifles and the manias buckled at the edge of dreamlessness.

After twenty or so treatments, I began consenting to the electroconvulsive therapy mostly for those conscious seconds before the Brevital Sodium took effect. I still wanted to die. I couldn't recall entire sections of my life. I could barely remember how to spell words like *receive* and *hollow*, but I found brief moments of peace before the Brevital blackouts. So I went to the hospital for as many blackouts as I could get, losing pieces of my mind with every treatment. Forgetfulness was just the price paid for the calm of a needle in the arm.

*

I became his new Old Lady only nine months after Possum's death. He'd been off heroin for six months. I'd been finished with electroshock therapy for four months.

By chance, we both found ourselves sitting across from one another at a dive bar, along with a few mutual friends. We drank Redheaded Sluts and discussed the merits of Robert Mapplethorpe. Later that night, we hopped into his rusted green pickup truck and let the chill of a Cleveland winter pull at the smoke of our cigarettes. The bars had all closed. The customers at the 24-hour greasy spoons had sobered up. We drove through the sleeping city to the base of the Hope Memorial Bridge, which rises more than 90 feet above the Cuyahoga River.

We're gonna climb it, he said.

I didn't mention my paralyzing fear of heights. I didn't mention my alcohol-induced lack of balance. I just followed him up the steel girders. My fingers numbed on the cold metal. My pants caught on a bolt and tore at the knee. A can of beer, which I'd placed in my pocket before climbing, fell to the ground and exploded with a skating violence. Beer hissed from aluminum. It foamed, it dripped, it went silent. I kept climbing, slightly disappointed by the loss of the beer.

The thing about amnesia is that you don't know what you've forgotten. You don't feel the memories slip from your pockets. You don't hear them hit the ground and hiss. They are there. And then they are not. You only know what you've lost by what others tell you, and you can only guess at the memories no one now recalls. You search your pockets for what's remained, piecing together a self with broken flashes and clouded scenes from a past that might have been yours. Are you a girl afraid of heights? Are you a girl who climbs bridges before sunrise? Have you done this before? He thought I was some daredevil tomboy who drank Redheaded Sluts and gloried in a predawn adrenaline rush. I wanted to be that self.

When we finally reached the beam meant for servicing the bridge, I could barely breathe from the fear of the climb.

The city stretched before us in the gray dawn.

He put his arms around me. I warmed my palms beneath his shirt. We stayed long enough to watch daylight filter through the streets, but the sun couldn't be seen through the clouds.

It was the morning of March 24, 2013—it would have been his seventh wedding anniversary with Possum. I didn't know this at the time. He never mentioned her name.

Nearly a week later, he moved in with me. There was little discussion. There was little consternation. He moved in and began sleeping in my bed. He moved in and began calling me his Old Lady.

She intrigues me, I've often said to those who've met Possum in passing. The most common response: *why?*

I heard stories about the pet turtle she let roam around her house, which purportedly caused houseguests to contract pink eye. I heard stories about the time someone tried to clean spilled watermelon off Possum's kitchen floor. Possum tore at her hair, screaming, *Don't clean my motherfucking house!* I heard stories about the time she unsuccessfully tried to poison her husband with antifreeze.

I heard stories about the times he'd tried to get clean. She'd call him up, and he'd answer, and she'd say, *you're nothing but a pussy who can't handle his drugs.*

I heard that she was bad news.

Was she pretty? I sometimes asked.

No one answered this question, so I searched for a picture online. I found a headshot of her on an old Myspace page. A shadow masked half of her face. Her hands were crossed over her chest, clutching a black shawl. Her lips were full, and the rims beneath her wide, green eyes were swollen. She was stunning in a Chelsea Hotel sort of way. A strung-out grace.

I heard stories about myself too. Many of these stories had been so thoroughly erased from my memory that I doubted their truth.

I heard stories about midnight skinny-dipping at Daytona Beach. I heard stories about eating conch balls in Key West. I heard stories about taking a mud bath in a San Francisco spa. Many of the positive moments—attending a writers' conference in Massachusetts, making hammocks in a Virginia commune—had slipped away into vague imaginings of what I must have been like. The more painful memories, however, seemed to have ingrained themselves too deeply to be uprooted. The high-school suicide attempts. The rape that occurred during my freshman year of college. I could still recall the scratchy textures of psych ward bed sheets, but I couldn't remember the Thanksgiving dinner when I laughed so hard that gravy seeped from my mouth.

And I wondered: what did it mean to be defined by your worst moments, your low points, your mistakes?

I knew Possum as a heroin addict. I knew myself as a bipolar mess. After finding that picture of Possum on Myspace, I developed a compulsion to learn more about her. I searched Google and Yahoo and MSN. I purchased a membership to Ancestry.com. I contacted police stations in search of arrest records.

I felt an obligation to record her, to establish a history other than the stories I'd heard. I wanted to believe in her life as something other than a disaster so that I could believe in my own life as the same.

After he and I had been dating for a few months, I began seeing possums everywhere. Beneath bushes. On sidewalks. Dead on the side of the road.

One evening, I walked into a garage. Flies swarmed my neck, my face, my arms. I found a dead possum in the corner, its body nearly disintegrated. I ran out of the garage, shaking with fear. I wondered whether his Possum was trying to send me a message. I began imagining his wife as some kind of demon. I imagined her as he dreamt of her: a woman intent on sabotage. Wicked. Malevolent. The hateful bitch. I spoke to a priest. He gave me holy water, which I sprinkled on the possum carcass before setting it out to be collected by garbage men.

I watched a possum scurry beneath a bush, skittish and vulnerable. Something fearful of predators. I imagined Possum on that night he wrote about in his journal—when she walked through his headlights wearing the vintage orange jacket that contrasted her green eyes. A striking woman with a light step. The type of woman who might disappear if you don't kiss her quickly.

I passed a dead possum on the road. Its body was bent and mangled. The flesh has begun to decay. I imagined Possum as an eight-year-old, wearing a flower-patterned bikini, running through a sprinkler, shrieking in the cold water. And I imagined her as an addict. Scoring, hooking, cooking her heroin in a spoon. I imagined her craving. I imagined the infected flesh at the bend of her elbow.

I found a vintage orange coat lined with fur in a thrift store. I immediately balked. *This must be her coat,* I thought. *This must be the coat that so perfectly contrasted her green eyes.* For a moment, I was too afraid to touch it. Was this coat a curse? A haunting? A friend of mine picked up the coat and insisted that I put it on. I did, and it fit perfectly. *That coat was made for you,* my friend said. I admired it in the mirror. My eyes are also green. I reached into the pocket, but my hand slipped all the way through. My friend bought the coat and insisted I keep it.

On Possum's birthday, I found a penny in my closet. It was heads up. *Lucky penny,* I thought. I remembered a myth I once heard as a child. Heads-up pennies are messages from the dead. If the date on a lucky penny matches the birth year of a dead relative or friend, it means the person is looking after you. I examined the penny. It was from 1979. The year of Possum's birth.

My obsession with her grew. I considered a séance, but I was too afraid. Instead, I imagined her. I created her in my own mind. I imagined that she hated me for taking her husband. I imagined her scowl. I imagined her disgust. I imagined her as a witch. I imagined her as a medicine man. I imagined that she has entered me, possessed me. We were inseparable. I imagined that *he* was not my lover, *she* was. She was some kind of soul mate I couldn't find in time. In a past life, she was my wife, my husband. In a past life, she was my mother, my daughter. Now she followed behind my shoulder, waiting to be recognized. I imagined that she wanted me to be a successful writer, a traveler, an adventurer. I imagined she wanted me to be what she couldn't be. And I imagined myself as what she was. I imagined myself as a heroin addict, even though I've never picked up a needle. I imagined myself selling my body for drugs, even though I don't know the price of sex. I imagined myself as a woman who traverses the country with little fear. I wore my vintage orange coat lined with fur and pretended to not feel fear.

I spent hours imagining. I spent hours dreaming up. I drove to the grocery store so lost in imagining that I had no idea how I'd arrived. We are made of our memories. When those are taken, it is easier to get lost in the imaginings than face a reality where we no longer know what we are.

I heard a rumor that Possum's graffiti was still present on the wall of a bathroom stall in a local dive bar. I took a friend to the bar to investigate.

What are we doing here? she said.

We're looking for my boyfriend's dead wife's graffiti, I said.

You're so creepy.

Perhaps so. After all, I was stalking a dead girl. But I wanted to touch something Possum had touched. Something other than her husband. Something stable and inanimate. In my mind, the graffiti would solidify her as more than a memory in the process of being forgotten.

Well, what exactly am I looking for? my friend said.

She just wrote her name.

I ran my finger past the *Fucks* and *Damns* and declarations of undying love written by urinating drunks. I paused at every jagged letter, but there was no sign of Possum's name.

I don't think it's here, my friend said.

Let me look a little longer.

I searched the entire bathroom twice more. My friend crossed her arms, impatient. She didn't seem to understand that I needed to find this graffiti. I needed to touch some tangible evidence of Possum's existence—something independent of another person's recollection. To do so would make my own amnesia seem less bleak. If the memory of a dead heroin addict could remain on a bathroom stall, then maybe my own memories were merely hidden, waiting to be unearthed.

Listen, my friend said, touching my elbow, *I think you're too late.*

Around the time I began seeing possums, he began calling me the perfect girlfriend.

You're never a bitch, he said. *You don't nag. You don't give me shit. You're not like all the other bitches out there. You're the perfect girlfriend.*

So I assumed that role. The more he told me I was perfect, the more perfect I became. The more he told me that I wasn't a nag, the less of a nag I became. I needed a role. I needed a self. The self I had before the electroshock therapy didn't seem to fit. I was told that I was an intellectual, but I could no longer remember the plot of *Hamlet* or the point of *The Republic.* I was told that I was a writer, but I couldn't spell words that a fifth grader could pen with ease. I was told that I was a sweet girl, but I often fantasized about murdering the handsome doctor who'd electrocuted my brain.

The perfect girlfriend, however, I could believe. I was very good at not being a bitch.

He added to the reasons for my perfection: I was flexible and agreeable. I didn't complain about PMS. I didn't check up on his whereabouts. I didn't accuse him of infidelity even when he made eyes at barflies and barkeeps. I was fun and adventurous and interesting. He took me to a park in the woods and prompted me to climb a nearly vertical rock that rose some thirty feet in the air. I began climbing, but I stopped halfway up, terrified. My fingers dug into sandstone. I couldn't breathe. My vision narrowed. *You have to keep going,* he said. *You can't go back now.* So I kept going. Beside his easy confidence, I could climb the rock. Beside his poise, I could be the life of the party. Beside his apathy, I could let myself relax. Beside his humor, I could be witty. Beside his experience, I could be a girl who scaled bridges at dawn.

I became the perfect girlfriend. I slipped into that identity. I put on that shell. The perfect girlfriend was fascinating and levelheaded and desirable. She was demure and helpful and hilarious and beautiful. She was not shrill. She was not irritating. She was not offensive. And she most certainly was not mentally ill. She did not have bipolar disorder. She did not put rifles in her mouth. The perfect girlfriend did not need electroshock therapy. She did not end up in psych wards. She was perfect. I was perfect, so long as he said so. And I did everything I could to keep him saying so.

When he spilt beers on the floor, I'd clean them up. When he whispered *cunt* to me in the privacy of our bedroom, I laughed it off. When he compromised hundreds of pages of my writing by watching anal porn without virus protection on a computer I repeatedly asked him not to use, I made only the smallest protestation. If I broke down in tears, I did so beneath a bathtub full of water. It was a slow suffocation of the self beneath the shell, but it was more comfortable to drown in his perfect version of who I should be than refashion the flawed version of who I was.

The stories I heard about Possum often began with a disclaimer: *I don't want to speak ill of the dead, but…*

This disclaimer always led into a story about Possum as a bitch, or an addict, or an occasional whore.

I don't want to speak ill of the dead, but…

But.

But I knew there were other stories. There were moments for which she wasn't given credit.

He occasionally spoke of his memories in the plural.

The best rack of ribs I had was in Missouri, he said. *We were broke and starving, and we stopped there. It cost sixteen dollars. The best fucking ribs ever.*

I always assumed that Possum was the other person present in such stories:

We stopped at the Indy 500. It was like Hillbilly Mardi Gras.

We used to smoke weed out of this bowl that someone had carved into a sandstone cliff in San Diego.

When he spoke poorly of her, she was the *Ex-Old Lady,* or the *Ex-Wife,* or the *Hateful Bitch.* But in the fond memories, she was always only the other half of his *we.*

I went with him for a walk at two in the morning in Clearwater, Florida. We'd been together for nearly a year. We were drunk and vacationing with his family. I was in a foul mood, although I tried to be chipper. I tried to be what he wanted me to be.

Less than two weeks prior to this vacation, he got blackout drunk and pissed on the gifts I had bought my family for Christmas. When I became upset, he said I was ruining his holiday. I had no reason to be angry. So I smiled. I acquiesced. I returned all the urine-soaked presents for non-urine-soaked presents. I made sure we had a nice Christmas. But my smiles were becoming more difficult to force.

As we walked the Florida streets, he said that he wasn't having a good time, because I was in a bad mood. I had almost ruined his holiday, and now I was ruining his vacation.

Without thinking, I stopped in the middle of the sidewalk and squared my shoulders.

Maybe you should find someone who's in a better mood, I said.

I said nothing more. I turned and walked in the opposite direction of our hotel. I didn't look back. He didn't follow. For the first time in months, I felt relief. An opening of my chest. An ability to breathe. It was not the kind of relief I used to experience in the seconds before the Brevital Sodium rendered me unconscious during electroshock therapy. It was less ethereal than the cusp of a blackout. It was the relief of being alone and alive and answerable only to myself.

As I walked forward, something hunched and white moved in the corner of my vision. My breath caught. I stopped dead. A possum stood in my path. We stared at one another for a moment, both of us startled.

Don't go back, something inside me said. *Don't go back, don't go back.*

At first I thought it was Possum's voice, or God's voice, or the Universe's voice, but it was my own voice, clear and insistent. It had been a long time since I'd heard that voice. *Don't go back.* The possum scurried into the bushes.

The following evening, I bought a single Greyhound ticket from Florida to San Francisco. I would leave him and traverse the country on a trip that would take nearly four days. I would no longer be the perfect girlfriend. I no longer knew what I would be. This was a terrible, gut-wrenching relief.

Nine months before I became his Old Lady, Possum called him from San Diego. They were separated at the time, and he was living in Cleveland.

Meet me in Vegas, she said. *We'll have a good time.*

It took some convincing, but he agreed. Maybe they could have another reconciliation. Maybe this one would stick.

She boarded a Greyhound bus, which rolled toward Vegas in the heat of a Southern California summer. She walked into the bathroom, sat on the toilet, and searched her scarred veins for the best place to insert the syringe. The heroin relieved her, but whatever euphoria she felt wasn't from the drug. She was traveling to see her husband. She was going to touch his bearded cheek and smile into his blue eyes. Maybe he'd meet her at the bus station, embracing her without saying a word. Maybe he'd kiss her recklessly, and onlookers would envy the way he cradled her head between his tattooed hands. Maybe they'd be man and wife again—two forces against the world.

Her eyes closed as the bus rumbled forward.

When the Greyhound reached Orange County, a fellow passenger realized that the woman with the striking green eyes hadn't come out of the bathroom. Someone forced open the door, but Possum was already gone.

I boarded the Greyhound in the evening. I found a window seat and angled my body in such a way that the other passengers couldn't see my face. Before the bus pulled out of the station, I began crying. Snot dripped down my chin. I didn't reach to wipe it away.

I cried for all those reasons that leaving a man is difficult, but I also cried for the memories I never mourned. I cried for ever having consented to electroshock therapy. I cried because I already knew the story he would tell our mutual friends. He would tell them that I was a hateful bitch for leaving him in Florida. Mostly, however, I cried for my tiny, flayed, evaporated self that could no longer hide behind what he said I was. A self blinking and disoriented. A self with an illness. A self too knotted to ever be one thing.

The bus pulled onto the street and headed north.

When I regained my composure, I opened my wallet to count what little money I had. As I flipped through a few bills, I came across the memorial card from Possum's funeral. Weeks prior, I had found the memorial card amid his personal items. I placed the card in my wallet, not to hide it from him but to save it for myself.

There is a black-and-white photo of Possum on the front of this card. Her dark hair frames her high cheekbones. Her eyes are bright and wide. She looks nothing like the strung-out woman in the Myspace picture. I wanted to remember her in this way. I wanted to remember her as someone poised and beautiful. And she was. She was poised and beautiful and adventurous in ways I will never be able to imagine. Perhaps she was once the little girl in a flower-patterned bikini jumping through the sprinkler. She was smiling and gorgeous and addicted and a whore. She was a hateful bitch and a manipulative disaster. A track-marked wreck. Full of grace.

I folded the card in half and placed it back in my wallet. The sun began to set behind highways lined with palm trees. The bus crept toward the coast. I watched the passing horizon, imagining the white-capped waves of the Pacific, anticipating the self I might be when I arrived.

EMERGING WRITER'S CONTEST WINNER
POETRY

In poetry, our winner is **Rosalie Moffett**, for her poems, "Why Is It the More," "To Leave Through a Wall," and "Hurricane, 1989."

Ploughshares' poetry editor, John Skoyles, writes: "Rosalie Moffett's poems are thoughtful and wise, dramatic and stunning in their perceptions. She handles huge issues (God's place in the universe; a lost twin; a mother's injury) with fresh strategies. That she can end an emotional poem with an image from a cartoon, and make it mov-

ingly effective, is a testament to her craft. Her poems make you want to say them aloud, to declaim them—to see what it's like to *be* her speaker. She has created a world that beckons the reader, not only to enter, but to enter and leave transformed."

Rosalie Moffett received her MFA from Purdue University, and is currently a Wallace Stegner Fellow at Stanford University. She is the winner of a "Discovery" / Boston Review poetry prize, and her poems and essays have appeared in *AGNI, The Believer, FIELD, Gulf Coast, Tin House,* and the anthology *Gathered: Contemporary Quaker Poets.* She lives in Oakland, California.

"My family is made up, mostly, of biologists, and my mother is a neurologist," Moffett writes. "Sometimes I think that the poems I'm writing about her brain put us on a convergent course; she progresses in her knowledge about the nervous system on one path, and I progress on another. I don't know what it will be like when we meet up. I suppose one hopes (if one has hopes for heaven, which I vaguely do from time to time) that that's what heaven is: all the different methods of thinking and knowing intersecting. Poems, I think, are little efforts in this direction."

ROSALIE MOFFETT

Why Is It the More

Syria Civil War Scars Captured by Satellite in Space
—NBC News Headline

                    I see of the world—heavenish
periscope of technology—the less
I can imagine God
                    intervening. Isn't it right to think that
given the whole thing at once,
we'd make out
                    some pattern we've been so far
too small to see? Flying out of Spokane,
the hills I grew
                    up in become doubtless
ripples, left behind by some giant
iceberg. That's what
                    I mean. To see the hand of the giant.
I'm sure there is someone
close by to tell me this
                    is ill-guided. This hope, this wrong
way to go about it. That no
matter what you think
                    you see you never
grasp the scope of what we're doing
to each other—
                    or undoing, or praying in our colorless
prayers. That is the muffling of being
small and human
                    and prone to peace
of mind. I don't understand why I give myself lectures
like this, the someone

I've imagined nearby for this sole
purpose does not look like any God
I know or one
that shaped an earth.

ROSALIE MOFFETT
To Leave Through a Wall

Twenty-five years ago in Galveston, Texas: helmetless,
my mother fell backwards

off her bicycle and hit her head. A hurricane
struck, tossing some cars

into the ocean. Everyone evacuated
while she waited in the hospital, wondering what

was the word for that, again? *To empty a town.* The names
of her children straggled back to her

city one by one while on the top floor
of a Dallas hotel, we watched Inspector Gadget's

fingers turn into flashlights. We knew
we fled, in heavy traffic, a storm

but not that we had been cast out
of our mother.

Anyone can pass through a doorway.
I always wanted to leave

through a wall, breaking
cartoonlike, a perfect body-

shaped hole. This is the only way,
isn't it, to know how to return exactly

to the same place as
the same person.

ROSALIE MOFFETT
Hurricane, 1989

It's as if all the roads between a thing

and its name dissolved. Texas 87 was washed
into sand, entirely. Our flimsy rented house

was intact, the little yard leaping with fleas, just

as we left it. She was home. She looked the same
but you could watch her feel

around for a word, as if along a wall

for a light switch. We waited
at stop signs: empty intersections, blank, whole

minutes passing. *The brain has to beat down*

new paths. Uncanny: highway
87 never was rebuilt—too close

to the gulf, to the rising water. And now *She is*

losing her marbles is how
my father puts it. His way

of not looking. (Of looking so

at it.) We have in our hands what
the MRI made of her

brain: something like a sliced loaf of bread.

I examine a piece, having nowhere
to put it: my mother's machinery, intricate map

of white lines, one where I must

in some form, reside. *I don't immediately see
any soft spots*—The Specialist,

pointing, hopeful—*where we look
at memory.* But I feel

very soft, or I hardly feel at all.

CARETAKER, MURDERER, UNDERTAKER
A Plan B Essay by Sherrie Flick

In the Plan B essay series, writers discuss their contingency plans,
extraliterary passions, and the roads not traveled.

Dirt rounds the ridges under my fingernails, making crusty silver moons. I try to clean up before I go out, but once I'm settled at the restaurant, I look at my hands and start to pick at the crud. I notice a smear of green on my calf, a smudge of yellow on my skirt. I tuck the hem under my thigh. What is that? I don't know, but I know where it came from.

When people who don't garden think of gardens, I imagine they imagine straight lines, tidy vegetables, and reasonable, reliable, hoed dirt. I see them seeing a steady, predictable rate of cultivation that leads to their lunch, dinner, future snacks.

But that isn't how gardeners garden. When I close my eyes and think about my garden, I inhale a glorious jumble of earth and rot and chaos. I see baskets of tomatoes, bushels of green beans. I exhale. I inhale.

In my garden, things reseed—borage, cilantro, dill. They do this here and there in convenient and inconvenient places. They also do it unpredictably from year to year. There are multiple planted patches of carrots, broccoli, kale, and Swiss chard. Too many tomato plants staked and strapped to the fence. Volunteer butternut squash vines creep through the arugula. Perennial flowers—lilies and irises, echinacea and black-eyed Susans—pop up each season in the middle of the vegetables and herbs. Blackberries loop and cane themselves into the tiger lilies, into the potato bin. There are some straight rows, yes. But that isn't the point.

What is the point? I'm not sure, but it's something instinctual. Some kind of primal drive to fill and create and make flourish and then— well—kill and eat all that stuff that comes from the ground.

A gardener is caretaker, murderer, and undertaker. We work toward death. On the way to harvest, we drown bugs and chase groundhogs. We throw rocks. We actually throw rocks. We make elaborate deer deflectors with Irish Spring soap and tin pie pans and human hair. And then we put everything to rest and begin again.

Hearing my neighbor shoot the bunny with a BB gun? Honestly? I'm relieved. The bunnies are too cute for me. The bunnies win every time in my garden, but not in my neighbor's, and for that I am thankful.

I remember the first time I actually wanted to strangle a deer with my bare hands. It had daintily consumed all of my hard-to-grow heartbreakingly beautiful light yellow heart-shaped heirloom tomatoes right off the vine, leaving just the vine—vibrant green and inedible. No tomatoes.

Even a baby deer. I would have strangled it.

I'm a vegetarian. You need to understand these garden impulses are impulses that pulse outside of my ethics. In my real life, I type on a computer. I listen to NPR. I cook a lot and can set up a mean *mise en place* on my cutting board. I play ukulele and drink red wine and Manhattans. I read books, play Scrabble. I stay pretty clean. Wear lipstick when I get dressed up. I don't touch spiders. I squeal when I see a snake or a mouse. I don't believe in the death penalty or animal cruelty or guns.

But still. I want to destroy that which destroys my kingdom.

This past year, I let a carrot go to seed in giant, flowering, amoeba-like blooms. These tendrils looked aquatic out there as they bobbed and ducked at the chicken wire fence, so uncarrot-like. I couldn't bear to pull it up. It grew and grew and now it will become next year's carrots—reincarnation. I am god here. But I'm not religious either.

Gardening has created in me a kind of fevered unleashing, an opening up. I kill the bugs that try to kill my vegetables, and then I kill the vegetables too and eat them.

If I had a redo, if I had one of those chances to change that you sometimes read about—*a lawyer becomes a baker! an accountant becomes a rock star!*—I would become a farmer. It would change me totally. I understand this.

In the garden, as I work, big bumblebees and skinny honeybees hum beside me. In a frenzy, they poke every single bloom in sight. They are ecstatic over the sunflowers this year. They are, I am certain, ODing on the sunflowers. I've never seen anything like it, except maybe at that one party in New Hampshire in 1989.

And then it's a gloriously sunny midsummer day—spears of sunlight sneak down through the sorghum leaves as I thin the beets.

That's when I see the spider—I mean, it's a giant arachnid. She has housed herself in the Brussels sprouts plant with an elaborate cone-like web. I learn later that she's an Orb Weaver. Right now she is furry and mighty and waving her many arms at me, as if to say: GET OUT. With only an ounce of a shudder, with zero squeal, I say to myself: Good. That's good. She's *good*. A good guy. Mean, but good. And I keep working. Same with the giant robotic-faced praying mantis. Same with the thin black snake I see slithering down under the raspberry bushes. *Good guys*. Good.

I reach for a tomato and my thumb plunges into the splotchy moldy goo that covers its underside. I wipe my hand on my shorts. Later, inside, my hands will be coated in yellow pollen, as if the garden has gilded me, changed my skin into pollen-dusted sandpaper.

Tiny, bulleted gold eggs make a tidy triangle on the back of my zucchini leaves. I rip the leaf and drown the eggs. I smoosh and smear until I feel feral. Bowls of beer drown the slugs. We call the bowls slug parties. We do.

Sometimes when I come inside sweaty and dazed, I look at myself in the mirror and, for a moment, I don't know who I am. My eyes have become electric blue and I am so alive with dirt and life that I glow.

I know if I were a farmer and not just this urban-gardener-on-a-slightly-larger-scale, I would eat meat. I would have to. I would grow cows and chickens; and how would they eventually be so different from the vegetables I kill on a daily basis? How would wringing one of their necks be different from twisting an ear of corn from its stalk? Some days my hands tingle with this knowledge. The power of cultivation. The power of knowing life and death. BAM—I smash the cucumber beetle against the wooden post. SNIP—I get that cabbage moth before it flits away.

I transport the ladybug gently, carefully over to the green beans, and I drown thousands upon thousands of stink bugs in soapy water each early morning. The dew glistens on the grass, and my little Yorkie runs to bark at our next-door neighbor, again. The bee balm and chamomile sway in the breeze. A neurotic hummingbird takes a big interest in the balm's bright red petals. Darting, darting. Traffic from downtown Pittsburgh's commuters zips and unzips on the parkways down the hill. They inch along like the ants on my peony buds. The crickets kick in, sounding like tiny car alarms.

Typing this essay in my nice clean living room, I feel a little itchy. I do feel bad some days for all of those stink bugs. I do. In general, I am a kind and generous person. But just today I saw a troop of tiny stink bugs on my scarlet runner beans and I said out loud: "Get the fuck away from my beans."

I harvest the vegetables and I make delicious fresh meals and canned goods for my husband and friends. I compost what is left over after the prep. Those leftovers break down and rot in the big black container in my yard, until they aren't recognizable. Until they pass over to become nutritious dirt. Healthy, beautiful compost that I spread across the beds as I get ready for next growing season. Always cycling everything around in a big, heaving, wriggling worm-filled circle that brings me back to life.

Sherrie Flick received a 2013 Golden Quill Award from the Western Pennsylvania Press Club for her food writing in Pittsburgh Quarterly *magazine and has written essays for the* Pittsburgh Post-Gazette *and* Superstition Review. *She is author of the novel* Reconsidering Happiness *(Bison Books, 2009), the flash fiction chapbook* I Call This Flirting *(Flume, 2004), and a forthcoming short-story collection due out from Queen's Ferry Press in March 2016. She lives in Pittsburgh and teaches in the Food Studies and MFA programs at Chatham University.*

DANCING IN A BOX

A Look2 Essay on Rhina P. Espaillat
by Nancy Kang and Silvio Torres-Saillant

The Look2 essay series, which replaces our print book reviews, takes a closer look at the careers of accomplished authors who have yet to receive the full appreciation that their work deserves. Reviews of new books can still be found on our blog at blog.pshares.org.

The small tasks of daily life may sometimes be regarded as an impediment to the large task of literary creation. Novelist Philip Roth, living alone in Vermont, once boasted of having reached a kind of ideal solitude. With "no one else to be responsible for or to, or to spend time with," he enjoyed total control over his schedule. Biographer Judith Thurman attests to the writer's peculiar happiness; divested of "[c]omplicated domestic arrangements, and the needs and conflicts of family life," all that remained was "this one thing: the work." Roth affirmed with pride, "I rule everything else out of my life. I didn't always, but I do now."

There is, however, another kind of writer, one who embraces the responsibilities that come with human interdependence. When such writers produce art—and it is often slowly, and late in life—there can be a richness that comes from the long period of being devoted, willingly and joyfully, to other matters.

The poet Rhina Polonia Espaillat is the second kind of writer. An American poet born in the Dominican Republic and raised in New York, she achieved early stardom as a teenager writing in Manhattan, but then her creative efforts slid into dormancy. Her marriage to then-teacher and now respected sculptor Alfred Moskowitz in 1952, and the dual task of raising a family and teaching English in New York City public schools, took priority.

After thirty years devoted to teaching and raising her three sons, Espaillat began writing poetry again and published *Lapsing to Grace,* her first collection of poetry, in 1992 at the age of sixty. Since then, she has published several other collections, including *Where Horizons Go* in 1998, which won the T. S. Eliot Prize that year.

Her late blossoming raises the question of the poems that may have been lost during the four decades of silence between her early literary celebrity and her first collection. Espaillat, however, considers it no sacrifice, and her attitude shows a very different philosophy from Roth's notion of art as solitary work to which one must be fanatically devoted. Instead, Espaillat celebrates patience and the value of keeping one's footing in the everyday. Of her years spent caring for her children, she remarks, "Of course raising them took time, but was time well spent and worth any number of poems. I think that the things a woman does that keep her from writing may frustrate her in the short run, but in the long run they contribute to the poems that she may eventually write. They provide the roots in daily living that keep poetry—all writing—from being self-referential and esoteric." As friend and fellow poet Alfred Nicol observes, "She resists the commonly held belief that domestic responsibilities have an oppressive and entirely negative effect on the creative spirit."

Espaillat's poetry, to date, despite achieving critical acclaim, is still too little known to the American reading public. This is simply a matter of exposure, because her work is deeply approachable and filled with both intelligence and emotion—a valuable counterweight in a poetic landscape that has become, at times, too abstract for many ordinary readers to navigate. In the words of poet and editor X. J. Kennedy, who awarded *Where Horizons Go* the T. S. Eliot prize, "All in all, it's a collection likely to persuade readers who think they don't like poetry that they do, after all."

Espaillat was born in the Dominican Republic's capital city of Santo Domingo in 1932. She was the only surviving child of diplomat Carlos Manuel Homero Espaillat and Dulce María Batista, a couple with cultivated tastes as readers of literature and a deep appreciation for their Hispanic heritage. Espaillat credits her paternal grandmother with fostering her early love of language. Apolonia Brache Ramírez (Mama Pincha) was a midwife by trade but also a poet who created an ambience in her household that celebrated literary and musical creativity, often inviting guests with artistic interests to come to her home for impromptu recitals and readings. The ambience nurtured in Rhina an early love for the written word. Before she could even write, the young girl would speak her poems and Mama Pincha would transcribe them for her.

Her maternal grandmother, Mama Julia, however, was a subservient and downtrodden woman, whose repressed silences and compulsive caretaking of others emerge with searing economy in the sonnet "Find Work," first published in *Poetry* in 1999 and later reprinted in *Her Place in These Designs* (2008):

My mother's mother, widowed very young
of her first love, and of that love's first fruit,
moved through her father's farm, her country tongue
and country heart anaesthetized and mute
with labor. So her kind was taught to do—
"Find work," she would reply to every grief—
and her one dictum, whether false or true,
tolled heavy with her passionate belief.
Widowed again, with children, in her prime,
she spoke so little it was hard to bear
so much composure, such a truce with time
spent in the lifelong practice of despair.
But I recall her floors, scrubbed white as bone,
her dishes, and how painfully they shone.

Mama Pincha, affectionately called "the woman with silk hands" by her clients, energized herself through creative hobbies and the company of life-affirming friends, while Mama Julia threw herself into the work of the home. Espaillat dedicated *Her Place in These Designs,* a woman-centered collection, to her two Dominican grandmothers who, according to the dedication, conferred to their granddaughter "clear and complementary notions of [her] place."

Espaillat seems aware that she inhabits the center portion of a Venn diagram created by these two matriarchs, willingly putting aside her own ambitions for numerous years while attending to domestic duties, but never relinquishing the attraction to art and its capacity—like a midwife—to usher forth new life.

When Rhina was five, the comfortable life of the Espaillat family in La Vega province ended. They left home to serve in the Dominican Embassy in Washington, D.C. Soon, her diplomat father's fall from grace with Generalissimo Rafael Leónidas Trujillo would cause the family to settle permanently in New York City two years later. Living in Manhattan, her father was now consigned to such jobs as mannequin assembler and porter, while her mother worked as a dressmaker.

Once in the metropolis, as her parents rebuilt their lives as working-class immigrants, Espaillat abided by her father's stern language policy that forbade anything but fully grammatical Spanish at home. Even so, she quickly excelled in English, producing her first Anglophone poem at age ten, a still extant text that meditates on nature, one of the favorite topics of her later verse.

As a result of her family's cultural pride and domestic language policy, however, Spanish never became for Espaillat a lesser language. She remembers that for Don Homero "the words in his own language were the 'true' names for things in the world," and that "if it could be said at all, it could be said best in the language of those authors whose words were the core of his education." Espaillat, of course, did not inherit her father's linguistic fundamentalism; her education brought her into contact with more nuanced thinking about the nature of language. But she does uphold his conservative sense of language as a legacy requiring protection from contamination: "I mean by bilingualism…what my father meant by it," she writes, "the complete mastery of two languages, with no need to supplement either one by injecting into it words from the other, either orally or in writing."

The recollection of her father's position on language has occupied Espaillat in two memorable texts, one a poem and the other an essay. Both entitled "Bilingual/Bilingüe," they appear in her second book of poems, *Where Horizons Go*. The poem is as follows:

My father liked them separate, one there,
one here (allá y aquí), as if aware

that words might cut in two his daughter's heart
(el corazón) and lock the alien part

to what he was—his memory, his name
(su nombre)—with a key he could not claim.

"English outside this door, Spanish inside,"
he said, "y basta." But who can divide

the world, the word (mundo y palabra) from
any child? I knew how to be dumb

and stubborn (testaruda); late, in bed,
I hoarded secret syllables I read

until my tongue (mi lengua) learned to run
where his stumbled. And still the heart was one.

I like to think he knew that, even when,
proud (orgulloso) of his daughter's pen,

he stood outside mis versos, half in fear
of words he loved but wanted not to hear.

When her first poetry books appeared and she began to accrue rec-
ognition from various critics, Espaillat could not count on a significant
number of Spanish speakers among her readers. As she never lived in a
Hispanic ethnic enclave, her closest cultural tie to her ancestral culture
was largely her periodic attendance at the Spanish Repertory Theatre.
She did retain fluency in Spanish, her mother tongue, and continued to
enhance her command of it for the sake of "treating the language well."
Readers of her first poetry collection, *Lapsing to Grace*, whom one
would assume to be primarily monolingual native English speakers,
may have been at a loss for what to do with "Nosotros," "Resignación,"
"Quise olvidarte, Dios," and "No le entristece al ruiseñor su suerte,"
four Spanish-language poems that appear in the book unaccompanied
by corresponding English translations.

Subsequently, reading about the publication of a Spanglish
dictionary and "wondering what could be the need for such a book,
and what might result from it," Espaillat immediately thought of
what her father would say, and the musing resulted in a third text

dedicated to her father's views on language. Entitled "An Imaginary Dialogue," the piece evolves as a conversation between Don Homero and his daughter. It repeats the belief that indiscriminate mixing of words from two languages has an inevitably impoverishing effect on both by causing "words in one to drive out perfectly good equivalent words in the other. The habitual speaker of such a mix ends by speaking not two, or even one complete language, but fragments of two that are no longer capable of standing alone." Espaillat's father in "An Imaginary Dialogue" bewails the mistreatment of both languages that occurs with the flourishing of Spanglish. The young particularly will lose out, he claims, for they will "finally find themselves without mastery of a single language, having wasted the magnificent opportunity to master two. The language of Cervantes, of Neruda, of Darío and Borges and Sor Juana, and yes, of Don Pedro Mir, deserves better treatment; and so does the language of Shakespeare, and Walt Whitman, Emily Dickinson, and Robert Frost."

Espaillat's literary trajectory began at Julia Richman High School in Manhattan in 1947, when her English teacher, a published poet named Catherine Hayden Jacobs, played a mentoring role. Known by her students as "Miss Jones," Jacobs successfully submitted some of Rhina's poems to *The Ladies' Home Journal,* enabling the fifteen-year-old to break into print. The following year Espaillat became the youngest member ever inducted into the Poetry Society of America after Jacobs, a member, showed a batch of her student's compositions to the organization. Subsequently, Espaillat's short poem "The Pigeons" was published as part of an interview in the January 4, 1950, final edition of the *New York Sun.* In its musicality, prosodic dexterity, thematic predilection for family matters, and use of animals to convey emotion and ironical humanity, this early poem foreshadows Espaillat's poetic maturity:

A lady, proud in poverty,
Fine but underfed,
With wary and disdainful eye,
Scans my gift of bread.

A cautious hop from sill to sill,
A peck, a warning note—
Love draws the lady back to fill
Two small and raucous throats

Her success continued while at Hunter College of the City University of New York, where, an English major, she studied poetics under Marion Witt, a brilliant and dynamic professor whom Espaillat remembers fondly as someone who "made every poem she discussed feel as if it had just been written that moment, specifically for us."

In 1952, one year before her graduation from Hunter College, Espaillat wed Alfred Moskowitz, a junior-high industrial arts teacher and the son of Jewish immigrants from Romania. Because her father was a "card-carrying atheist" and her mother more inclined toward Buddhist philosophy than the traditional Catholicism that dominates the Dominican Republic, Espaillat did not encounter family resistance to her interfaith marriage. Moskowitz had served in World War II, returning in the spring of 1946 with memories of the Battle of the Bulge, and was actually the fourth man to propose to Rhina. Two she had rejected "easily," but the third, a pen pal from South Dakota, expressed reluctance at having a wedding in New York; he preferred to marry and settle in his home state, making the poet nervous about maintaining her close family ties. On the other hand, Moskowitz was not only supportive of her family and her art, being an artist himself, but he also encouraged her to keep her maiden name because it was the one with which she had established her reputation up to that point.

After receiving her degree, Espaillat taught junior high school English. In 1954, the first of her two biological sons, Philip, was born. In 1956 came another son, Warren; both grew up to attend the Massachusetts Institute of Technology and became physicists. She wrote very little during this time, but she did return to school to earn an MSE from Queens College in 1964. In 1968, a foster son, Gaston ("Bill") Dubois, whose photograph of a busy Grand Central Station graces the cover of Espaillat's fourth book, *The Shadow I Dress In* (2003), came to live with the Moskowitz family. From then on, parenting and home-making would coalesce into her primary occupation.

For fifteen years, she taught English at Jamaica High School, a position she held until she left the profession to return to poetry in 1980.

Her domestic duties grew increasingly complicated by the task of adult caregiving as well, since the growing dependence of her Alzheimer's disease-stricken mother necessitated a move from New York to Massachusetts where her now adult children resided.

In "Workshop," a poem written in 1985, Espaillat explores the tension between the demands of the craft and the extratextual world. The poem, she has explained, provided a vehicle for her to undertake "a reexamination of [her] life, and an assessment of the relationship between any creative pursuit and the time-consuming daily human experience out of which, after all, art is made." It begins with "'Where have you been… / 'and what have you been doing?'" questions asked by an old friend who remembered her from the literary circuit decades earlier. Experiencing each question as one that "weighs and measures" her like "an unpaid bill," she lists a few of the tasks that have kept her busy:

Well, I've been coring apples, layering them
in raisins and brown sugar; I've been finding
what's always lost, mending and brushing,
pruning houseplants, remembering birthdays

The poem's fourth stanza captures the way the concentration required by the job of parenting shaped her way of knowing the world:

Spoon-fed to me each evening, history
puts on my children's faces, because they
are the one alphabet all of me reads

The closing of the poem seamlessly connects the exigencies of daily life with the art of writing. Life is a sort of "workshop" that contributes to literary training, imaginative engagement, and final execution, all on one's own terms and in one's own time:

I've been setting the table for the dead,
rehearsing the absence of the living,
seasoning age with names for the unborn.
I've been putting a life together, like
supper, like a poem, with what I have.

Returning to the craft of poetry after retirement from teaching, she felt "glad to discover that the ability to write is as enduring as the desire." Almost sixty at that point, Espaillat produced copiously and with equal vigor sent out work, especially to venues that had shown a taste for rhyme and meter, such as *Sparrow, The Formalist, Orbis, Blue Unicorn, The Lyric, The American Scholar,* and *Plains Poetry Journal,* among numerous other literary journals and magazines.

She also realized the wisdom of creating communities as a way to catalyze poetic activity. Collaboration, criticism, and mutual support marked her creative methodology; she chose interpersonal experiences over isolation. The Fresh Meadows Poets is a group that Espaillat cofounded in Queens in 1986, which very actively organized readings and workshops, and in so doing, helped increase Espaillat's contact with fellow artists. Leaving a lasting impression on that literary scene, Espaillat had already relocated to Newburyport, Massachusetts, by the time *Lapsing to Grace* was released in 1992. In that seaside city, she had also started an organization with the mission "to unite local poets and provide a supportive environment for them." Named after "a tributary to the Merrimack River that flows through extensive wetlands where birds and wild mammals abound," the Powow River Poets run a monthly reading series and a poetry competition under the auspices of the Newburyport Art Association, an institution that had not made much noise in the city before Espaillat arrived in 1990. When the group published *The Powow River Anthology,* edited by Nicol, a chorus of twenty-four poets who had participated in its activities over the fifteen years of its existence, it seemed natural to dedicate the volume to the vivacious and generous Espaillat.

Although an exception to her wider critical acclaim, a dismissive review of Espaillat's collection *Playing at Stillness* (2005) in *Poetry* magazine by Dan Chiasson might indicate some reasons for her having received less attention than she deserves. While Chiasson alleges that the poems are filled with "small kindnesses," he declares them not weighty enough, and that Espaillat's "humble 'answers'" fail to demonstrate the abstraction, experimentation, and high seriousness reflective of the Modernist legacy. With this review and others, we encounter a critical stance that construes Espaillat's oeuvre to be "old-fashioned," largely due to her deployment of received forms rather than free verse, and the assumption that such forms are arcane, conservative, and politically suspect. Espaillat's output thus straddles the debates around New Formalism and the "Free Verse Establishment." She scoffs at the idea that preset forms like the sonnet, villanelle, and sestina are reactionary or ideologically problematic, remarking in a January 2013 interview at her Newburyport home, "The fact is that you can find as many left-wing formalists as you can find right-wing free-versists."

Suggesting that Espaillat's work lacks seriousness is myopic. One simply needs to look closely at the harmony of content and form rather than focus on Modernist expectations. *Lapsing to Grace,* for instance, gathered a series of individual poems that dramatize moral quandaries of various sorts; a prime example, "Incident" (sharing the title of Countee Cullen's 1925 poem of a child's shattering confrontation with racism), has its speaker suspect herself of insensitivity when, in the subway, a stranger asks her for a coin and she reacts by taking another seat and looking resolutely away. Other works capture moments of everyday domestic experience, encounters that occur casually but have enormous significance. "Calculus," for one, recalls a conversation with her youngest son, at the time a graduate student. When he tries to explain to her the rudiments of formulae using visual imagery, she realizes these were rhetorical devices close to her poetic way of knowing the world. She finally started to understand, recalling, "The pleasure of that quiet conversation, the affectionate humor of my son's attempt to help me understand a difficult mathematical concept by means of visual imagery, became, for me, a metaphor for the nature of love, which reaches so tenaciously across distances of all kinds."

Another major thematic strand in her larger body of work is to be found in a series of poems that enmesh the nature of craftsmanship and commitment to a particular art form. "Being the Ant," drawing from Aesop's fable "The Ant and the Grasshopper," presents readers with the ambivalence that often comes from our comparing ourselves to those in possession of talents, resources, and circumstances different from (and usually better than) ours. The ant regards himself in contradistinction to the grasshopper, someone whom he perceives to be enjoying a greater degree of public affection. But the miniscule speaker squashes the temptation to concentrate too much on his imagined adversary:

To tell the truth, although I like his voice
I have no time for envy, having much
to do storing the nest against harsh days
from which sweet singers think themselves exempt.

Ultimately, we can never tell whether we have a better or worse
bargain than a person brandishing a different kind of craft:

Do I regret my role in his demise?
Well, yes and no. Let's say it's what I do,
and what one does is what one is at last,
as bronze becomes the form in which it's cast.

As a longtime mentor to other poets, Espaillat's reflections on form
and composition are of particular value. On the basis of his affiliation
with the Powow River Poets, Kennedy described her as the "spark
plug of the group, a kind of bardic queen bee or aesthetic den-mother,
a teacher by vocation and by nature and, as many fellow poets will
attest, a generous friend." In a Truman State University interview in
1998, Espaillat offered an exhortation that reads as an eloquent *ars
poetica*. It brings together an appreciation of recognized poetic struc-
tures with the individual's talent:

> *Don't be afraid of tackling formal structure, which is a challenge
> and a delight, like the arbitrary rules of any game worth playing:
> there would be no pleasure to any game if it didn't entail the risk
> of losing, and if there were no obstacles to keep you from winning.
> It's impossible to "think outside the box" unless you first have a
> box to get outside of! The pleasure of poetry is that you first get
> to make the box (by learning how to build it, with language) and
> then willingly climb into it, then tempt the reader into it with you,
> and then manage to get out of it without destroying it, all while
> dancing. It's one of the oldest arts, after all, and art is the only ac-
> tivity I know of that can take a profound sorrow and turn it into
> an artifact that inexplicably provides comfort without changing
> anything.*

Already past her eightieth year, on June 1, 2013, Espaillat attended a panel dedicated to her work within the program of the Latin American Studies Association Conference held at the Marriott Wardman Park Hotel in Washington, D.C. Her husband Alfred, celebrating his eighty-eighth birthday on that very day, took pictures of the proceedings and exuded unmitigated joy at the occasion. In the audience were conference participants who had chosen the session because of their admiration for Espaillat as a formalist and well-loved American poet. Others came attracted by her ethnic ties to the Hispanic and specifically Dominican-American subdivisions of American literature. The questions and comments that followed the presentations by the panelists led to an animated discussion of the dual place that she occupies in the United States' literary landscape. They pointed to the composite facets of her literary persona: on the one hand, she enjoys distinction as a highly regarded voice of the New Formalists, a cohort of poets normally associated with a mostly white mainstream. On the other, she plays a key role as a Latina and a committed advocate of her ancestral cultural heritage.

Espaillat's active engagement with ethnic advocacy has manifested itself primarily in a sustained effort to disseminate the writings of Hispanophone poets from all periods, as well as her undaunted support of Dominican immigrant writers, especially those from Massachusetts and New York. During the panel in the nation's capital, Espaillat offered insights that readers of her work had no problem recognizing as part of a familiar credo. Overall, she articulated her integrative vision of culture, language, ethnicity, aesthetics, identity, and the power of poetry and the arts to build bridges of communication among humans across varying levels of difference. The relocation to Newburyport not only brought Espaillat into contact with a community of peers and her dynamic leadership in the Powow River Poets, it also brought her close to the Dominican immigrant enclave of nearby Lawrence, Massachusetts, where a group of cultural activists, with poets César Sánchez Beras and Juan Matos among them, regularly meet for readings and recitals, primarily in Spanish. She connected with them and began a relationship of productive collaboration that has included her participation as a founding member of the board of the Pedro Mir Literary Workshop, named after Pedro Mir (1913-2000), a revered poet from the Dominican Republic.

She has long been unequivocal about taking stock of her ancestral roots. Unlike William Carlos Williams, for instance, whose Puerto

Rican mother and her tropical culture only surface after a close scrutiny of his biography and a search for clues in his poems, Espaillat easily conveyed her background from the outset. Dominican roots and a love of the Spanish tongue stand as vital aspects of her Anglophone poetics. Increasingly cultivating her skill as a translator over the last decade, she has produced stellar Spanish renditions of poetry by Frost and truly compelling English-language versions of the poetry by the Iberian mystic Saint John of the Cross (San Juan de la Cruz). In terms of intergroup cultural advocacy, Espaillat has instituted the practice of having Anglo participants from Newburyport featured in the Hispanic programs organized by the Dominican immigrant writers in Lawrence. Conversely, Hispanic writers from Lawrence now occasionally appear in the mostly Anglophone readings of the Powow River Poets in Newburyport. It is a productive braiding of language, love of poetry, and regional communion.

Having spent the first six decades of her US experience in the mosaic-like boroughs of Manhattan and Queens, Espaillat had much to draw from when she urged her audience, during a 2006 speech at Hostos Community College of the City University of New York, to think of identity "not as something we have, but as something that happens to us." In one poem entitled "Cartography," she recalls her grandfather's family tree ("Spaniards, Africans, Frenchmen, nameless Arawaks") and then grafts her affiliations onto the ancestors of her husband, Alfred ("blessed in Hebrew, beside Rumanian rivers"). Her imaginative canopy is one that covers the United States and encompasses generations, races, and religions, as well as degrees of closeness: "Children, asleep, breathe stillness, but in their bones / an endless knitting takes place, a long forgiveness: / slaver and slave, Jew, Christian, stranger and stranger."

Comfortable with her layered identity, Espaillat upholds the most expansive vision of "Americanness." She identifies this as being "a person with a foreign background who grew up speaking English and some other 'mother tongue,' who has relatives elsewhere and profound emotional ties to some other place, but who is mostly wholly 'home' in the United States, in its language and ideals." Although brought up in the first half of the twentieth century, Rhina P. Espaillat has come into the twenty-first century uniquely equipped with the accoutrements required to speak eloquently about an ethos of integration.

She inhabits her ethnicity, linguistic self, gender, aesthetics, individual relationships, community belonging, and biological being with a verve and confidence that fuse easily and yet with porosity. Her work points to a world of capacious coexistence where difference rarely interferes with the possibility of harmony.

Nancy Kang, Assistant Professor of English at the University of Baltimore, is co-author with Silvio Torres-Saillant of the forthcoming book The Once and Future Muse: Poetry and Poetics of Rhina P. Espaillat. *Her work has appeared in such journals as* African American Review, Women's Studies, *and* Canadian Literature.

Silvio Torres-Saillant, Professor of English at Syracuse University and Associate Editor of the journal Latino Studies, *is the author of* Caribbean Poetics *(Peepal Tree Press, 1997, 2013)*, The Dominican-Americans *(Greenwood, 1998)*, *and* An Intellectual History of the Caribbean *(Palgrave-Macmillan, 2006)*, *among other books.*

Zacharis Award

Zacharis Award *Ploughshares* is pleased to present Roger Reeves with the twenty-fourth annual John C. Zacharis First Book Award for his poetry collection, *King Me* (Copper Canyon, 2013). The $1,500 award, which is named after Emerson College's former president, honors the best debut book by a *Ploughshares* writer, alternating annually between poetry and fiction.

This year's judge was John Skoyles, *Ploughshares'* poetry editor. In choosing the book, Skoyles said: "The poems in Roger Reeves' *King Me* are lively, intelligent, and dramatic. They possess an astonishing range, richly populated by the things of this world. Open the book anywhere, and you will touch and be touched by a startling image, statement, or object. These poems would overflow their forms if not for Reeves' ability to harness their power into tight and explosive lines. *King Me* is down to earth, tough, tuneful, and wise."

Awarded a 2014-2015 Hodder Fellowship from Princeton University, a 2014 Pushcart Prize, a 2013 National Endowment for the Arts Literature Fellowship and 2008 Ruth Lilly Fellowship, Roger Reeves' poems have appeared or are forthcoming in *Best American Poetry, Poetry, American Poetry Review, Boston Review,* and *Tin House,* among other publications. *King Me,* his first book of poems, was published by Copper Canyon Press in 2013. *King Me* has been awarded the 2014 Larry Levis Reading Prize by the creative writing program at Virginia Commonwealth University and the PEN Oakland/Josephine Miles Literary Award. He is an assistant professor of poetry at the University of Illinois at Chicago.

What was your early life like? What was your first exposure to poetry?

My earliest exposure to poetry was a mash-up of Dr. Seuss and the King James Version of the Bible. I grew up in a pretty religious household (Pentecostal), and my mother was a Sunday School teacher. Often, on Fridays and Saturdays, I hung out with my mother while she prepared her Sunday School lesson, so my first real exposure to poetry and writing and the magnificence of the written word was as a critic. And because there was no separate Sunday School for children in my church, I learned to read and think about texts while watching adults grapple with the ineffable, faith, and the mysteries of a Judeo-Christian god. But what I remember most was the weeping and transformation. Often, I watched churchgoers, brothers and sisters, come to some epiphany about their own life because of the text. I know, I know, very reader-response of me, but I didn't know to look at the scene with a more fashionable post-structural eye.

What sent me into poetry—the ability of the word (written and spoken) to transform—is what keeps me here now. As a child, I was fascinated by passages like the Tower of Babel and the Day of Pentecost. Both of those passages highlight the difficulty of language and the power of ecstatic speech. Though I had no clue what they meant, I loved the Song of Solomon as well as David's psalms. So these were my first poems, my first exposure to poetry.

When did you start reading and writing seriously? What was the first poem that you remember meaning something to you?

I decided to be a writer when I was 16. I had just flunked an AP History timed-essay exam. I wrote nothing in the forty minutes of allotted time. Often, I clammed up. Sure, a few fits and starts, but I always crossed out the passages, never satisfied with the writing. So I had written nothing on this exam, and I remember walking down the hall of my high school to my journalism teacher's room, Mr. Connolly, and declaring through teary eyes that I wanted to be a writer even though I had just failed this timed-essay exam.

Mr. Connolly gave me some of the best writing advice I ever received: "Just write. Then revise." And then, he offered to look at any writing I did. And he was a merciless editor. Red all over the page. But when I started to give him poems, there was much less red and more comments concerning the meditations. It was the first time that I understood writing to be a dialogue with a reader.

The first poem that meant something to me was a Kenneth Koch poem because it was "postmodern" and crazy, which appealed to my seventeen-year-old self. I can't quite recall the title of the Kenneth Koch poem, but I remember feeling like it gave me permission to write whatever I wanted and needed to write. I went home that night, waited for everyone to go to bed, and wrote until 2 or 3 in the morning. It was spring. I remember hearing the universe for the first time. It buzzed. I'll never forget that moment. This might sound overly romantic, but I'm always listening for that buzz.

When did this collection start taking shape? What were some of your inspirations?

The manuscript started taking shape late summer 2011. I was at the Bread Loaf Writers Conference, and I took a manuscript shaping workshop with Tom Sleigh. Sleigh began the workshop on manuscript shape by discussing literal shapes—lines, spirals, circles, curves. He was speaking my language. I understand the world via shapes and geometric objects. And it was the first time I heard someone discuss a manuscript's trajectory in this manner. For a long time, because I saw so many books with sections, I tried to force my book into sections. But as Sleigh introduced to me, sections are important for a book, necessary for the book, if they teach the reader how to understand the arc or trajectory of the book.

In the workshop, Sleigh handed out tables of contents of different poetry books—Elizabeth Bishop's *Geography*, *The Iliad*, and a few others I can't remember. What I remember most was realizing that my book didn't have to look arc-wise like other books and that it needed to find its own logics. I realized that the book hovered around certain obsessions. That's when I realized my book's shape was more like a sine curve with troughs and peaks. So I literally used the shape of a sine curve to lay it out on the floor of my apartment in Chicago.

Some of my inspirations for the book, for thinking about the making of the book were Jean-Michel Basquiat and his deformation of mastery, lynching, family, home, our many loves and lovers.

Who are some of your favorite poets, and which influences do you think appear most powerfully in this collection?

My favorite poets probably shift depending on the time of the day, but at the time of writing *King Me*, the poets I constantly returned to were Terrance Hayes, Natasha Trethewey, Tracy K. Smith, Brigit Pegeen Kelly, Dean Young, Larry Levis, John Ashbery, W. B. Yeats, John Berryman, Carl Phillips, W. H. Auden, Pablo Neruda, and Federico García Lorca. Which influences do I think appear most powerfully in this collection? That's such a difficult question to answer because I think of my influences as a weave, a very tightly woven weave, wherein it's quite difficult to pull one thread out and say "ah, that's it, that's where the tapestry begins."

However, I can point to lines from other poets that sent me into poems. For instance, the title of the poem "When I Come to the Valley of the Black Pig" comes from a poem by Yeats. Neruda's *Twenty Love Poems and a Song of Despair* offered a presiding aesthetic consciousness in some of the "love" poems in the books. Some of the formal concerns—meter, received form, line—are in direct conversation with Yeats, Stevens, and Trethewey. However, I think of poems as an amalgamation of influences, of conversations, or replies of sorts.

Your work moves from pop culture to politics to history (often, it seems, the history of tragedies) and finally to what might be called "high culture," sometimes within a single poem. Talk about this mix, and how it reflects your preoccupations and interests as a writer.

I find the distinction between "high" and "low" to be rather arbitrary. For instance, opera was not always high culture, and now it is. Shakespeare's plays weren't always high culture, and now they are. All culture and its attendant appendages are contested. And it is that contestation and conversation that I'm most interested in. There's aesthetic energy, restraint, complexity in all cultural forms and productions. How that rigor is displayed, played with, troubled, dissembled, funked up, is often what I'm interested in as a writer. As aforementioned, we are all a collision of influences, and I happen to believe these influences offer both aesthetic and intellectual appeal. Mike Tyson tending to his pigeons in Brooklyn teaches me as much about the ethics and erotics of care as Toni Morrison writing about mother tending to a reincarnated ghost. Both of these moments are spaces of lyric energy. Each moment teaches about craft and what it is to make.

Have there been any surprising reactions to King Me *since its publication? Are there any observations you've heard that you perhaps didn't recognize while writing?*

Yes and no. I knew that there would be poems that challenged my readers because of the way in which they embrace abjection and grapple with intimacy, often simultaneously. Most people like to keep pain as far away from them as possible. And concomitantly, most folks like to keep beauty close. I understand the impulse. However, I wanted to play with both of these impulses in the text. A poem like "Cross Country" often causes many people to cringe and even put the book down. I was aware that this poem might have this effect. In fact, in trying to publish "Cross Country" in journals, editors often replied that they liked the poem most, but they felt some anxiety publishing it. Ah well.

However, what I have found most odd but totally pleasing is the way the book has been embraced by high-school students, folks in communities that I never thought the book would reach, like Cedar Rapids, Iowa. I did a reading out there, in Cedar Rapids, and this older white woman who was a journalist during the Civil Rights Movement grabbed my arm very gently after the reading and talked to me about the movement and how she wished it could have done more for African Americans. I have had an opportunity to talk about the book with men in prison through letters and e-mails.

What have you been working on recently? And how do you tend to write (in terms of times of day, materials, routines)?

I have been working on a book-length poem and a novel. I don't like to do too much telling or describing of work-in-progress, because I find that description can over-determine the project. I like to follow and attend to the work rather than intend anything. I write at any time during the day. I perform the morning brain, that right-out-of-the-bed-the-dream-world-and-logic-still-with-you brain. I try to be as flexible as possible, to not be too prescriptive about what I need in order to write. It keeps the pretensions and mystery out of the work. Writers write. You sit down (or stand) and move a pen (or typing cursor) across the page. However, I do have preferences that I am learning help to ease me into writing, like a closed door, mountains, big open spaces, elevation, nature (both sublime and picturesque). But those are preferences, not requirements in the least.

*Book Recommendations from
Our Advisory Editors*

Ann Beattie recommends *Next Life Might Be Kinder* by Howard Norman: "Novels never mean to untangle complexities that exceed their bounds, but this post-Freudian masterpiece is hardly a shrug. It's a humane, mystifying, demonstrable declaration of the borders of unknowability, written by one of our most provocative and daring writers." (Houghton Mifflin Harcourt, May 2014)

Stuart Dybek recommends *The Lovers Set Down Their Spoons* by Heather Slomski: "Each story is located in a subjective sphere that is reproduced with keen attention to objective reality and the tension between those, thanks to Slomski's gracefully lucid, lyrical prose." (University of Iowa Press, October 2014)

Stuart Dybek also recommends *Three Scenarios in Which Hana Sasaki Grows a Tail* by Kelly Luce: "If from the title of the book and the name of the press that published it, a reader might think invention, wit, and the fabulous might be at work here, that reader would be right. The book is written with great charm. It is worth the price of admission just to read the last story, 'The Amorometer,' a piece I felt compelled to teach in my undergrad workshop." (A Strange Object, October 2013)

Philip Levine recommends *The Fever Chart* by Naomi Wallace: "Wallace calls her three short plays 'Visions of the Middle East.' I have not seen them on stage, but reading them I found it easy to enact them in my head. The dialogue is brilliant, often poetic without ever resorting to an elevated diction. Individually each play feels complete to me; together they are overwhelming. The first two involve Israelis & Palestinians, & she sees all the characters with great empathy & insight. The third is the monologue of a twenty-something Iraqi survivor attending an international pigeon convention. It is the single most imaginative & powerful piece of writing I have read for ages." (Theatre Communications Group, July 2009)

Thomas Lux recommends *Blood, Sparrows and Sparrows* by Eugenia Leigh: "A first book by a young poet that strikes me as original, fearless, and highly accomplished." (Four Way, October 2014)

Elizabeth Spires recommends *The Theme of Tonight's Party Has Been Changed* by Dana Roeser: "This is a book of startling, almost dizzying juxtapositions, wide in scope and deep in feeling. Roeser is interested in mirroring the rapid, unpredictable movement of the mind as it finds similarity in dissimilarity, always the poet's task. One of the pleasures of reading this collection may be in the way the poems both amuse and alarm as they capture the texture and split focus of contemporary experience. I can't think of anyone who writes better about the anxiety that fuels modern life." (University of Massachusetts Press, January 2014)

Maura Stanton recommends *Mimi's Trapeze* by J. Allyn Rosser: "As soon as I finished reading this book of brilliant poems, I wanted to read it again. So will you." (University of Pittsburgh Press, August 2014)

Gerald Stern recommends *The Astonished Man* by Blaise Cendrars: "I highly recommend reading *The Astonished Man*, which I am rereading, again." (Peter Owen Modern Classics, April 2004)

Jean Thompson recommends *Lay It On My Heart* by Angela Pneuman: "*Lay It On My Heart* creates a world where religion both sustains people and undermines them. Its thirteen-year-old narrator is perfectly balanced between belief and rebellion, and we root for her all the way." (Mariner, July 2014)

Dan Wakefield recommends *Uncle Anton's Atomic Bomb* by Ian Woollen: "A compelling story of a family haunted by CIA contact. He is one of the few writers to 'get it right' about the mood and life of the '50s—and this three-generation family saga takes us into the '90s." (Coffeetown Press, September 2014)

Rosanna Warren recommends *Anti-Judaism: The Western Tradition* by David Nirenberg: "Much more than a history of anti-Semitism, this work examines the way in which people of different cultures in different eras have imagined Jews, even when hardly any Jews lived among them. From the Ancient Egyptians to early Christians through the Renaissance and into Modernity, the Jew came conveniently to represent whatever the culture most feared, its darkest imagination of the Other, its nightmare self-portrait. The book includes accounts of the relation of European medieval kings to "their" Jews (who often supplied them with funds), and of the consequences of the expulsion of Jews from Spain, and a remarkable rereading of *The Merchant of Venice*. Heine emerges as grimly prescient when in his *History of Religion and Philosophy in Germany* in 1835 he predicted that German philosophical distortions of Judaism could have dangerous consequences: 'Thought precedes deed as lightning precedes thunder...Such a drama will take place in Germany, that in comparison the French Revolution will look like an innocent idyll.'" (W. W. Norton, February 2013)

Eleanor Wilner recommends *Bridge* by Robert Thomas: "Ever wonder what that quiet girl in the office is thinking? The serial monologues of Alice, self-described as an 'irrational prime number,' place us inside a wholly original, slightly suicidal, radically unconventional mind: precariously balanced, yet how far down she can see without falling. In this poet's tour de force fiction, Thomas' imaginative language created in me, to transplant his phrase, 'what medical books accurately term prolonged dazzle.'" (BOA Editions, October 2014)

Al Young recommends *Sweetness #9* by Stephan Eirik Clark: "Think: *Stalag 17*, *Catch-22*, *Slaughterhouse-Five*, the Clovers' 'Love Potion Number 9' and you're right on trail. Stephan

Eirik Clark's Vonnegutesque novel about a conscientious food flavorist and the family he spawns knocked me out. Delivering a rich, in-depth story—satirical yet naturalistic by turns—*Sweetness #9* spans more than four decades (1973-2012). I laughed, gulped, and gasped at how accurately this shattering send-up tracks the last third of the 20th century, the so-called American Century, and the US appetite for artificially flavored foodstuffs and superficial living. A splendid, engrossing read." (Little, Brown, August 2014)

EDITORS' CORNER
New Works by Our
Advisory Editors

Amy Bloom, *Lucky Us*, a novel (Random House, July 2014)

Robert Boswell, *Tumbledown: A Novel* (Graywolf Press, September 2014)

Ron Carlson, *The Blue Box*, poems (Red Hen Press, August 2014) and *Return to Oakpine*, a novel (Penguin Books, October 2014)

James Carroll, *Warburg in Rome*, a novel (Houghton Mifflin Harcourt, July 2014)

B. H. Fairchild, *The Blue Buick: New and Selected Poems* (W. W. Norton, July 2014)

Mary Gordon, *The Liar's Wife: Four Novellas* (Pantheon, August 2014)

Kathryn Harrison, *Joan of Arc: A Life Transfigured*, a biography (Doubleday, October 2014)

Edward Hirsch, *Gabriel: A Poem* (Knopf, September 2014)

Lorrie Moore, *Bark: Stories* (Vintage, October 2014)

Carl Phillips, *The Art of Daring: Risk, Restlessness, Imagination*, essays (Graywolf, August 2014)

Ladette Randolph, *Leaving the Pink House*, a memoir (University of Iowa Press, September 2014)

Gerald Stern, *Divine Nothingness*, poems (W. W. Norton, October 2014) and *I'm Dancing with Tears in My Eyes*, drawings (University of Iowa Press, October 2014)

Mark Strand, *Collected Poems* (Knopf, October 2014)

Jean Thompson, *The Witch: And Other Tales Re-told* (Blue Rider Press, September 2014)

Colm Tóibín, *Nora Webster*, a novel (Scribner, October 2014)

Kevin Young, *Hungry Ear: Poems of Food and Drink* (Bloomsbury USA, October 2014)

CONTRIBUTORS' NOTES
Winter 2014-15

Keith Althaus is the author of two books of poems: *Ladder of Hours* (Ausable, 2005) and *Rival Heavens* (Provincetown Arts, 1993). He has curated exhibits at the Provincetown

Art Association and Museum, and the Fine Arts Work Center in Provincetown. He has poems forthcoming in *Plume*, *Hotel Amerika*, and *Phantom Limb*. He lives in North Truro, Massachusetts, with his wife, the artist Susan Baker.

Jeanne Marie Beaumont is the author of *Burning of the Three Fires* (BOA Editions, 2010), *Curious Conduct* (BOA, 2004), and *Placebo Effects*, a National Poetry Series winner (Norton, 1997). She coedited *The Poets' Grimm: 20th Century Poems from Grimm Fairy Tales* (Story Line Press, 2003), and teaches at the 92nd St. Y in Manhattan and in the Stonecoast low-residency MFA program.

Zeina Hashem Beck is a Lebanese poet with a BA and an MA in English Literature from the American University of Beirut. Her first poetry collection, *To Live in Autumn* (Backwaters Press, 2014), won the 2013 Backwaters Prize, judged by Lola Haskins. She's been nominated for a Pushcart Prize and her poems have appeared in *Nimrod*, *Poetry Northwest*, *The Common*, *Cream City Review*, *Copper Nickel*, *Mizna*, *The Midwest Quarterly*, and *Mslexia*, among other publications. Zeina lives with her husband and two daughters in Dubai, where she regularly performs her poetry. Her website is zeinahashembeck.com.

Remica L. Bingham-Risher earned an MFA from Bennington College, and is a Cave Canem fellow and a member of the Affrilachian Poets. Her first book, *Conversion* (Lotus Press, 2006), won the Naomi Long Madgett Poetry Award. Her second book, *What We Ask of Flesh*, was published by Etruscan Press in 2013. She is the Director of Writing and Faculty Development at Old Dominion University and resides in Norfolk, VA, with her husband and children.

Christopher Brunt is a fiction writer and poet whose work appears in *Drunken Boat*, *Bat City Review*, *Ovenbird*, and other publications. He is currently a Visiting Assistant Professor at the University of Houston Honors College, and is at work on a novel.

Christopher Buckley's 20th book of poetry, *Back Room at the Philosophers' Club*, was published in 2014 by Stephen F. Austin State University Press. He is the recipient of a Guggenheim Fellowship in Poetry, two NEA grants, and a Fulbright Award in Creative Writing. He received the James Dickey Prize for 2008 from *Five Points*, the William Stafford Prize in Poetry for 2012 from *Rosebud*, and he was the 2013 winner of the Campbell Corner Poetry Contest. With Gary Young he has edited *One for the Money: The Sentence as a Poetic Form* (Lynx House Press, 2012).

David Cameron lives with his wife and children near Boston, Massachusetts, where he works in higher education. His fiction has appeared in *Carve* magazine, *Digital Americana*, and *The Literary Review*. He is also the fiction editor for *Talking Writing* magazine. Find out more at davidcameron77.com.

Bruce Cohen's poems and essays have appeared in literary periodicals such as *AGNI, The Georgia Review, The Harvard Review, Ploughshares, Poetry,* and *The Southern Review,* as well as being featured on *Poetry Daily* and *Verse Daily.* He has published three volumes of poetry: *Disloyal Yo-Yo* (Dream Horse Press, 2009), which was awarded the 2007 Orphic Poetry Prize, *Swerve* (Black Lawrence Press, 2010), and *Placebo Junkies Conspiring with the Half-Asleep* (Black Lawrence Press, 2012). A new book, *No Soap, Radio!* will be published in 2015. A recipient of a grant from the Connecticut Commission on Culture & Tourism, he is presently a visiting professor on the Creative Writing faculty in the English Department at the University of Connecticut.

Tadeusz Dąbrowski is a poet, essayist, critic, and editor of the literary bimonthly *Topos.* He has been published in many journals in Poland and abroad. In America, these journals include *The New Yorker, Boston Review, Ploughshares, AGNI, American Poetry Review, Tin House,* and *Guernica.* His work has been translated into twenty languages. Author of six volumes of poetry in Polish, his American collection, *Black Square,* was translated by Antonia Lloyd-Jones and released by Zephyr Press in 2011. He lives in Gdańsk on the Baltic coast of Poland.

Sierra Golden received her MFA in poetry from North Carolina State University. Winner of the program's 2012 Academy of American Poets Prize, Golden's work appears or is forthcoming in literary journals including *Chicago Quarterly Review, Permafrost,* and *Prairie Schooner.* She has also been awarded residencies by Hedgebrook, the Island Institute, and the Sitka Center for Art and Ecology. Although she calls Washington State home, Golden has spent many summers in Alaska, working as a commercial fisherman.

Mary Gordon is the author of six previous novels, two memoirs, a short-story collection, and *Reading Jesus,* a work of nonfiction. Her most recent work is *The Liar's Wife: Four Novellas* (Pantheon, 2014). She has received many honors, among them a Lila Wallace–Reader's Digest Writers' Award, a Guggenheim Fellowship, an O. Henry Award, an Academy Award for Literature from the American Academy of Arts and Letters, and the Story Prize. Gordon teaches at Barnard College and lives in New York City.

Lisa Gruenberg is a physician working in Boston. *A Beautiful Day* is excerpted from her memoir, *Searching for Mia,* which is currently being considered for publication. She earned her MFA in creative writing from Lesley University's Low Residency Program in 2007. Her essays have been published in *The Intima: A Journal of Narrative Medicine* and *Vital Signs.* Her short story, *Keiskamma,* won the 2012 Massachusetts Cultural Counsel Artist's Fellowship. She is expanding this story, about an American doctor working and raising a family in South Africa, into novella form.

Kathleen Halme is the 2014 winner of the Green Rose Prize at New

Issues Press. The winning manuscript, *My Multiverse*, her fourth book, will be published in March 2015. Halme is a recipient of a National Endowment for the Arts Poetry Fellowship and a National Endowment for the Humanities Summer Fellowship in Anthropology. She lives in Portland, Oregon.

Jennifer Hanno is a short-story writer and English teacher who lives in the foothills of the Adirondack Mountains of Northern New York. She is currently working on a collection of linked stories featuring *The Case for Psychic Distance*.

Michael Hettich's books of poetry include *Like Happiness* (Anhinga, 2010) and *The Animals Beyond Us* (New Rivers, 2011), as well as the chapbook *The Measured Breathing* (Swan Scythe, 2011). His new book, *Systems of Vanishing*, won the Tampa Review Prize in Poetry and was published in April 2014 by the University of Tampa Press. He lives in Miami. His website is michaelhettich.com.

Nalini Jones is the author of a story collection, *What You Call Winter* (Knopf, 2007), and other short fiction and essays (in *One Story, Ninth Letter*, and *Elle India*, among others). She is a recent recipient of an O. Henry Prize, a Pushcart Prize, and a National Endowment for the Arts fellowship, and is currently at work on a novel.

Lisa C. Krueger is a clinical psychologist. Her poems have appeared or are forthcoming in various journals, including *Ploughshares, Prairie Schooner, Atlanta Review, Paterson Literary Review,* and *Rattle*. She is the author of three books of poetry: *Rebloom* (2005), *animals the size of dreams* (2009), and *Talisman* (2014), all from Red Hen Press. She has published articles and written a series of interactive journals related to psychology and creativity, and maintains a psychotherapy practice in Pasadena.

Ying-Ju Lai is from Taipei, Taiwan, and received her MFA from Boston University. She is currently working on a novel set in the Dutch Golden Age and contemporary Taiwan. She lives in Boston.

Lance Larsen has published four poetry collections, most recently *Genius Loci* (Tampa, 2013). He has received a number of awards, including a Pushcart Prize and a fellowship from the National Endowment for the Arts. In 2012, he was named to a five-year term as Utah's poet laureate. A professor at BYU, he recently directed a study abroad program in Madrid.

Philip Levine was born in Detroit in 1928. He is the author of twenty collections of poetry, and his honors include the Pulitzer Prize, two National Book Awards, and two National Book Critic Circle Awards. In 2011, he was named the 18th US Poet Laureate by the Library of Congress.

Antonia Lloyd-Jones is a full-time translator of Polish literature, and twice winner of the Found in

Translation award. She has translated fiction by several of Poland's leading contemporary novelists, including Paweł Huelle, and nonfiction including most recently *Gottland*, true stories about the Czechs, by Mariusz Szczygieł (Melville House, 2014). She also translates crime fiction, poetry, essays, and books for children and young adults. She is a mentor for the BCLT's Emerging Translators' Mentorship Programme, and a UK Translators Association committee member.

Wayne Miller's third and forth poetry collections are *The City, Our City* (Milkweed, 2011)—which was a finalist for the William Carlos Williams Award and the Rilke Prize— and *Post-* (2016; forthcoming). His translation of Moikom Zeqo's *Zodiac* will be published by Zephyr Press in 2015, and he has coedited three books, including the forthcoming *Literary Publishing in the 21st Century* (Milkweed, 2015). He teaches at the University of Colorado Denver and serves as Managing Editor of *Copper Nickel*.

Michael Morse lives in Brooklyn, New York, and he teaches at The Ethical Culture Fieldston School and The Iowa Summer Writing Festival. His first book of poems, *Void and Compensation*, will be out from Canarium Books in the spring of 2015.

Lex Runciman is the author of five books of poems, including *One Hour That Morning* (Salmon Poetry, 2014) and *The Admirations*, winner of the Oregon Book Award (Lynx House Press, 1989). His work has been anthologized recently in *40 Years of CutBank* (from *CutBank* magazine) and in *Alive at the Center: Contemporary Poems from the Pacific Northwest* (Ooligan Press, 2013) and he has new work forthcoming in *Nimrod, Stand,* and *Miramar*. He teaches at Linfield College.

Sherod Santos is the author of six books of poetry, most recently *The Intricated Soul: New and Selected Poems* (W. W. Norton, 2012). He is the recipient of the Theodore Roethke Memorial Prize and an Award in Literature from the American Academy of Arts and Letters. He lives in Chicago.

Laurie Sewall's poems have appeared or are forthcoming in *Hayden's Ferry Review, Cimarron Review, Poet Lore, Hawaii Pacific Review, Columbia: A Journal of Literature and Art,* and many other publications. She received an MFA in poetry from New England College and an MA in counseling psychology from Lesley University. She currently lives and teaches in rural Iowa.

Mairead Small Staid is a Zell Postgraduate Fellow at the University of Michigan, where she received her MFA. Her essays and poems can be found in *AGNI, The Believer,* and *The Southern Review,* among other publications.

Laura Van Prooyen, author of *Inkblot and Altar* (Pecan Grove Press, 2006), was awarded the McGovern prize from Ashland Poetry Press for her second collection of poems, *Our House Was on Fire* (nominated by Philip Levine); the book is set for release in January 2015. Recent work also appears in *The American Poetry Review, Boston Review,* and *The Southern Review,* among others. Van Prooyen teaches creative writing at Henry Ford Academy: Alameda School for Art + Design in San Antonio, TX. Her website is lauravanprooyen.com.

Matthew Vollmer is the author of *Future Missionaries of America* (MacAdam Cage, 2009), a collection of stories, and *inscriptions for headstones* (Outpost19, 2012), a collection of essays. With David Shields, he is the coeditor of *Fakes: An Anthology of Pseudo-Interviews, Faux-Lectures, Quasi-Letters, "Found" Texts, and Other Fraudulent Artifacts* (W. W. Norton, 2012). In 2015, Persea Books will publish his second story collection, *Gateway to Paradise.* He is the editor of *21st Century* Prose at the University of Michigan and directs the undergraduate creative writing program at Virginia Tech.

Afaa Michael Weaver (born Michael S. Weaver, 1951) is a native of Baltimore, Maryland. He has received prizes for poetry and playwriting, including three Pushcarts, Pew and NEA fellowships, a Fulbright appointment (2002) to teach in Taiwan, and the PDI Award in playwriting. His twelfth collection of poetry, *The Government of Nature* (Pitt, 2013) won the 2014 Kingsley Tufts Award, and his work is included in *Best American Poetry 2014.* Afaa's thirteenth and fourteenth collections of poetry are *A Hard Summation* (Central Square Press, 2014) and *City*

of Eternal Spring (Pitt, 2014). *City of Eternal Spring* completes his Plum Flower Trilogy, the other two books of which are *Plum Flower Dance* and *The Government of Nature.* He holds an endowed chair at Simmons College and teaches in Drew University's low-residency MFA program in poetry and translation. See his website at plumflowertrilogy.org.

Gary Young has been awarded grants from the NEA and the NEH. He's received a Pushcart Prize, and his book of poems, *The Dream of a Moral Life* (Copper Beech, 1990), won the James D. Phelan Award. He is the author of several other collections of poetry, including *Hands* (Illuminati, 1979); *Days* (Silverfish Review Press, 1997); *Braver Deeds* (Gibbs Smith, 1999), winner of the Peregrine Smith Poetry Prize; *No Other Life* (Heyday Books, 2005), winner of the William Carlos Williams Award; *Pleasure* (Heyday Books, 2006); and *Even So: New and Selected Poems* (White Pine Press, 2012). In 2009, he received the Shelley Memorial Award from the Poetry Society of America.

GUEST EDITOR POLICY

Ploughshares is published three times a year: mixed issues of poetry and prose in the spring and winter and a prose issue in the fall. The spring and fall issues are guest-edited by different writers of prominence, and winter issues are staff-edited. Guest editors are invited to solicit up to half of their issues, with the other half selected from unsolicited manuscripts screened for them by staff editors. This guest editor policy is designed to introduce readers to different literary circles and tastes, and to offer a fuller representation of the range and diversity of contemporary letters than would be possible with a single editorship. Yet, at the same time, we expect every issue to reflect our overall standards of literary excellence.

SUBMISSION POLICIES

We welcome unsolicited manuscripts from June 1 to January 15 (postmark dates). We also accept submissions online. Please see our website (pshares. org) for more information and guidelines. All submissions postmarked from January 16 to May 31 will be recycled. From March 1 to May 15, we also accept submissions online for our Emerging Writer's Contest.

Our backlog is unpredictable, and staff editors ultimately have the responsibility of determining for which editor a work is most appropriate. If a manuscript is not timely for one issue, it will be considered for another. Unsolicited work sent directly to a guest editor's home or office will be ignored and discarded.

All mailed manuscripts and correspondence regarding submissions should be accompanied by a self-addressed, stamped envelope (s.a.s.e.). No replies will be given by e-mail (exceptions are made for international submissions). Expect three to five months for a decision. We now receive well over a thousand manuscripts a month.

For stories and essays that are significantly longer than 5,000 words, we are now accepting submissions for *Ploughshares Solos* (formerly *Pshares Singles*), which will be published as e-books. Pieces for this series, which can be either fiction or nonfiction, can stretch to novella length and range from 6,000 to 25,000 words. The series is edited by Ladette Randolph, *Ploughshares* editor-in-chief.

Simultaneous submissions are amenable as long as they are indicated as such and we are notified immediately upon acceptance elsewhere. We do not reprint previously published work. Translations are welcome if permission has been granted. We cannot be responsible for delay, loss, or damage. Payment is upon publication: $25/printed page, $50 minimum and $250 maximum per author, with two copies of the issue and a one-year subscription. For *Ploughshares Solos*, payment is $250 for long stories and $500 for work that is closer to a novella. The prize for our Emerging Writer's Contest is $1,000 for the winner in each genre: fiction, poetry, and nonfiction.

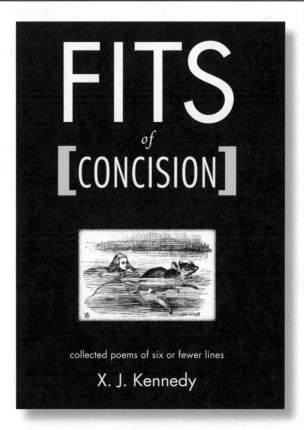

IR
INDIANA
REVIEW

Fiction
Poetry
Nonfiction
Artwork

SINCE
1 9 7 6

indianareview.org
inreview@indiana.edu

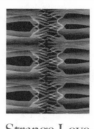

PLOUGHSHARES

Stories and poems for literary aficionados

Known for its compelling fiction and poetry, *Ploughshares* is widely regarded as one of America's most influential literary journals. Most issues are guest-edited by a different writer for a fresh, personal vision, and contributors include both well-known and emerging writers. *Ploughshares* has become a premier proving ground for new talent, showcasing the early works of Sue Miller, Edward P. Jones, Tim O'Brien, and countless others. Past guest editors include Raymond Carver, Kathryn Harrison, Seamus Heaney, Lorrie Moore, Derek Walcott, and Tobias Wolff. This unique editorial format has made *Ploughshares* a dynamic anthology series—one that has established a tradition of quality and prescience. *Ploughshares* is published in April, August, and December, usually with a prose issue in the fall and mixed issues of poetry and fiction in the spring and winter. Subscribers also receive an annual Omnibus that gathers together our Solos—longer form stories and essays originally published in digital form.

Subscribe online at pshares.org.

- -

☐ Send me a one-year subscription for $35.
  I save $27 off the cover price (3 issues and Omnibus).

☐ Send me a two-year subscription for $55.
  I save $69 off the cover price (6 issues and two Omnibuses).

Start with: ☐ Spring ☐ Fall ☐ Winter

Name _____

Address _____

_____

E-mail _____

Mail with check to: Ploughshares · Emerson College
120 Boylston St. · Boston, MA 02116

Add $35 per year for international postage ($15 for Canada).